D0119634

TACKLE ASTRONOMY THIS WAY

Tackle Astronomy This Way

H. C. KING

PH.D. M.SC., F.R.A.S., F.B.O.A.

STANLEY PAUL
London

STANLEY PAUL & CO. LTD
178–202 Great Portland Street, London, W.1.

London Melbourne Sydney
Auckland Bombay Toronto
Johannesburg New York

★

First published 1962

*This book has been set in Times New Roman type
face. It has been printed in Great Britain by The
Anchor Press, Ltd., in Tiptree, Essex, on Antique
Wove paper and bound by Taylor Garnett Evans &
Co., Ltd., in Watford, Herts*

Contents

Illustrations

Preface

For the greater part of its long history astronomy has had to depend upon what people could discover with the eyes alone. They studied the movements of the Sun, Moon, planets and stars right from earliest times, but the telescope was not invented until 1608, a fairly recent date in human history.

We too can learn a great deal about astronomy without hardly ever looking through a telescope. But we must look at the sky itself—it's no good shutting ourselves indoors and just reading books. Whenever possible we must check what we read with what we can see for ourselves in nature. In brief, our study of astronomy must be both an indoor and an outdoor activity.

This little book tells you what to look for in the night sky—what to expect to see and how to interpret what you see. It's not an elementary textbook or manual but a straightforward guide to personal enquiry and observation. It also touches on many of the things about which ordinary people ask questions—questions which are usually quite different from those which an astronomer might expect them to ask. It tries to put 'first things first' so that the final picture has the greatest possible chance of being as complete and as well balanced as possible.

We tackle first the movement of the sky itself, then the movements of the Sun, Moon and planets in the sky. What we find out is then applied to the way these bodies travel in space. We deal with other bodies too—with meteorites, comets and asteroids—learn about the stars as suns, the way they form vast systems called galaxies and how the galaxies form an even greater system called the Universe.

The approach all through is a practical one. It does not require the use of a telescope, although the reader will probably want to buy, make or borrow one. It's something which anyone can manage on his own, without any previous training in mathematics or physics, and without hardly any expense at all.

                                                    H. C. KING

Amersham, Bucks

continued out to this sphere, meets it at the two celestial poles. The Earth's equator, projected on to the sphere, forms the *celestial equator*. The study of the geometry of the celestial sphere is called *spherical astronomy*, a subject in itself and one closely allied with astro-navigation, or navigation by the stars.

For our purposes it will be sufficient to realize that the stars appear to move differently when seen from places well separated in latitude. Consider, for example, the appearance of the night sky from three places:

1. *The North Pole.* All the northern stars are on view. The north celestial pole is 90° above the horizon, which places it at the centre of the sky. During one rotation of the Earth the stars therefore appear to travel parallel to the horizon once round the sky.

2. *The South Pole.* All the southern stars are on view. No bright star indicates the position of the south celestial pole, which is 90° above the horizon. During one rotation of the Earth the stars therefore appear to travel in the same manner as they do at the North Pole.

3. *The Equator.* The north celestial pole is on the northern horizon, the south celestial pole is on the southern horizon. These points fix the direction of the Earth's axis. Hence, during one rotation of the Earth the stars all share in a general east-to-west motion. A star on the celestial equator rises straight upwards due east and sets straight downwards due west. From this position we can see both northern and southern stars, but at any one time, of course, only one-half of the entire celestial sphere.

It is therefore clear that if we travel northwards from the equator the north celestial pole and *Polaris* will rise higher and higher in the northern sky. Similarly, if we travel southwards from the equator the south celestial pole will rise higher and higher in the southern sky.

World-travellers can obtain first-hand experience of these things but most of us have to rely on the imagination.

There is, however, the modern planetarium and in this you can actually see in a matter of minutes the appearance of the night sky from any place on the Earth's surface. In addition, you can purchase a star globe or celestial globe, but good ones are rather expensive and they have the disadvantage of showing the celestial sphere as seen from the outside instead of as seen from the inside. This is where the planetarium instrument scores heavily, for it projects its stars on to the inner surface of a hemisphere, which then resembles the starry vault of the night sky.

Besides rotating on its axis the Earth also travels or revolves about the Sun. Hence, while the Earth's rotation brings about the succession of day and night its revolution brings about the changing seasons of the year. As far as the stars are concerned we have now to consider the *seasonal* change in the night sky.

As we travel about the Sun, so the Sun appears to move over the background of stars, making one full circuit of the sky in a year. In nature, of course, we do not see the Sun do this for the very good reason that we cannot see the stars in daytime. They fail to appear because they are so faint in contrast with the brighter blue curtain which characterizes the daytime sky at its best. This blue haze is produced by the scattering of sunlight as it passes through the Earth's atmosphere, the blue rays being scattered more than the rest.

In mid-winter, in the northern hemisphere, the Sun has as background the stars of Sagittarius, The Archer. Six months later, after the Earth has completed one-half of its annual journey, these stars lie in a direction opposite to the Sun. They can therefore be seen in the summer night sky, lying towards the south at midnight. Similarly, in spring, we cannot see the stars of Pisces, The Fishes, and of nearby Pegasus, because they lie near the Sun. Yet six months later, in autumn, these stars are over in the southern part of the sky at midnight. It will, of course, be obvious that many stars are always on view on a clear night, regardless of the season. *Polaris* is one, so in theory, at least, are all those seen from London which lie within the range $51\frac{1}{2}°$ of the north celestial pole. These stars are all *circumpolar* in that they not only wheel unceasingly about the north celestial pole but always remain above the horizon. In reality stars which just skirt the northern horizon are usually hidden from view by mist and haze or objects on the skyline.

The seasonal change in the appearance of the night sky is nicely demonstrated with a planisphere. This consists of a circular star map partly covered by an opening which represents the amount of visible sky. The circular map can be rotated and set for any time and day of the month. The stars which then appear in the opening correspond with those above the horizon at the particular time and date chosen. Very good planispheres are made by George Philip & Son, Ltd., the well-known cartographers at 32 Fleet Street, London. These are nicely produced in stout cardboard, cost only a few shillings and are available for the latitudes $51\frac{1}{2}°$N. and 35°S. Practise with one of these and then try it out on the natural sky as opportunities arise: you will be surprised how quickly you can recognize the main star groups and appreciate both the nightly and seasonal changes of the starry sky. If you happen to live in a latitude a few degrees away from that stated on the planisphere it can still be of immense help. It's just a case of remembering that the position of the celestial pole marked on the map should be slightly further from or closer to the nearest horizon.

Another way of seeing the seasonal change without having to wait a whole year is to visit a large planetarium. The planetarium instrument is so designed that a Sun can be projected on to a background of stars. It can then be moved so that the Sun moves across the stars, a movement which corresponds, of course, to that of the Earth about the Sun. It is also possible to bring about 'eternal day' and 'eternal night', that is, to show the changing appearance of the starry sky at either midday or midnight throughout a whole year. The movement is speeded up considerably, and the events of a year can be made to go by in a matter of minutes.

Since in nature the Earth takes a whole year to travel once round the Sun, the Sun, as seen from the Earth, moves slowly in a west-to-east direction at the rate of about 1° a day. This means that the Sun, on the average and

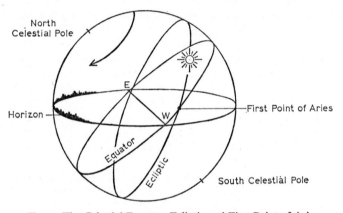

FIG. 1. The Celestial Equator, Ecliptic and First Point of Aries

relative to the stars, rises about 4 minutes later every day. Its apparent path or track among the stars is called the *ecliptic*. This imaginary line crosses the celestial equator in two places, being inclined to the equator at an angle of about $23\frac{1}{2}°$. This angle is called the *obliquity of the ecliptic*. Because of this the Sun's midday angular height above the horizon varies by as much as 47° throughout the year. In this connection the Philips' Planisphere is again of immense help, for it can be used to demonstrate both the daily and seasonal change in the Sun's angular height.

Let us now consider the Sun's behaviour at four special times of the year.

1. *December 22nd*. The time of the *winter solstice*. The Sun is $23\frac{1}{2}°$ south of the celestial equator and therefore furthest south. As seen from London he spends only a short time above the horizon, rising in the south-east and setting in the south-west. His greatest angular height, at midday, is only 15°. As seen from a place in latitude $23\frac{1}{2}°$ south, or on the Tropic of Capricorn, the Sun at midday is directly overhead. At this time of the year the north pole of the Earth is turned to the greatest possible extent away from the

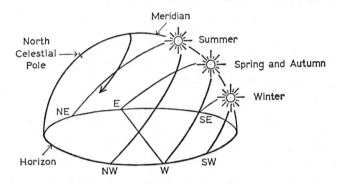

FIG. 2. Seasonal changes in the Sun's altitude at noon

Sun. The North Pole is half-way through its long winter of six months but the South Pole is enjoying mid-summer.

2. *March 21st*. The time of the *vernal equinox* or *spring equinox*. The Sun is about to cross from below to above the celestial equator. He is therefore at the 'First Point of Aries' or one of the points where the ecliptic crosses the celestial equator. As seen from London the Sun rises due east and sets due west. His greatest angular height at midday is $38\frac{1}{2}°$. The day is now equal in length to the night. As seen from a place on the Earth's equator the Sun at midday is directly overhead. Both the north and south poles now get equal shares of sunlight.

B

3. *June 22nd.* The time of the *summer solstice.* The Sun is $23\frac{1}{2}°$ north of the celestial equator and therefore furthest north. As seen from London, he spends his longest time above the horizon, rising in the north-east and setting in the north-west. His greatest angular height, at midday, is 62°. As seen from a place in latitude $23\frac{1}{2}°$ north, or on the Tropic of Cancer, the Sun at midday is directly overhead. At this time of the year the north pole of the Earth is turned to the greatest possible extent towards the Sun. The North Pole enjoys mid-summer but the South Pole is half-way through its long winter of six months.

4. *September 23rd.* The time of the *autumnal equinox.* The Sun is about to cross from above to below the celestial equator. As seen from various places on the Earth's surface, he behaves in precisely the same way as he did at the time of the vernal equinox.

Throughout the course of human history the stars have presented a seemingly changeless background. Yet, as we shall see later, the stars are moving suns, every one of them travelling through space at great speed. So far away, however, are the stars that only after careful observation over many years can astronomers detect any change in their relative positions. For our present purposes we can regard the stars as objects fixed for all time to the dome of the sky.

There is, however, an important change in that the star *Polaris* is only temporarily the North Pole Star. The Earth not only rotates on its axis and revolves about the Sun but, like a spinning top, it precesses or 'wobbles'. The wobble is a very slow one, one complete wobble taking as long as 25,800 years. As a result, each of the celestial poles moves in a circle around the corresponding pole of the ecliptic once in 25,800 years. It therefore points to different parts of the starry sky at different times. For example, about 5000 years ago, when the Ancient Egyptians built the great pyramids at Gizeh, the nearest bright star to the north celestial pole was not *Polaris* but a star known as *Alpha*

Draconis. At present *Polaris* is just under 1° from the north celestial pole and will come nearest to it in the year 2095. About the year A.D. 14000 the bright star *Vega* will feature as the North Pole Star. Associated with all this is the fact that the First Point of Aries moves along the ecliptic in an east to west or backwards direction at the rate of about $1\frac{1}{3}$° every century. The motion is called *precession of the equinoxes*, or, more briefly, *precession*.

From what we have so far said it will be apparent that the motions of the Earth are all reflected in the sky. When once you have obtained a clear picture of the effects of the Earth's daily rotation and annual revolution you have made a great step forward. But don't be content with the picture for just one particular latitude on the Earth. Try to get a more general picture by considering the ways the stars appear to move for places *anywhere* on the Earth. Help yourself by purchasing a small star globe, or, better, buy two planispheres, one for northern latitudes and one for southern latitudes. If you can, visit a planetarium (Plate 2), but do this after rather than before you have made some headway on your own. Your best training ground will always be nature's own sky. By night, notice how the stars appear to move across the sky, learn to spot the North Pole Star quickly, get to know the main circumpolar stars (these are described in our next chapter) and whenever possible during the year check on the general layout of the stars at a specific hour, say, midnight. Midnight or near midnight is a good time to choose because you then know that as you look towards the south (if you live in the northern hemisphere) you are looking directly away from the Sun. By day, notice whenever possible the directions of sunrise and sunset at different times of the year, also the height of the Sun at midday. A good idea of the latter is obtained not by looking at the Sun (always a dangerous practice) but by noting the lengths of shadows cast by familiar objects.

2

Star Patterns, Constellations and Star Names

TO APPRECIATE the way the sky changes during a night or throughout the year is to become familiar with the main star groups and patterns. Here again you will be helped by a planisphere and also by a star map or atlas. Some books on astronomy include directions for finding certain bright stars, while a few contain simple star charts, but a good atlas is always a sound investment. One of the clearest and most useful is *Norton's Star Atlas*, now in its 14th edition and quite low in price for its size and quality. It contains all the stars visible to the naked eye, showing them as black dots of various sizes on a white background, and covers the entire celestial sphere.

Near *Polaris*, and therefore in the northern part of the sky, lies a prominent star pattern. Seven bright stars form the figure of a plough and for this reason are often called the stars of The Plough. Different peoples at different times, however, have interpreted the figure differently. It has been called, among other things, The Great Saucepan, Charles' Wain or Charles' Wagon, The Ladle and The Big Dipper. But whatever interpretation you give these stars you will always find that the two at the end of The Plough's 'body' point unfailingly to *Polaris*. For this reason they are called 'The Pointers' and have been used for this purpose right from early times.

Since they all lie fairly close to *Polaris*, and therefore to the north celestial pole, the seven stars of The Plough are circumpolar for all places higher in latitude than about 45°N. That is to say, they can be seen from these places

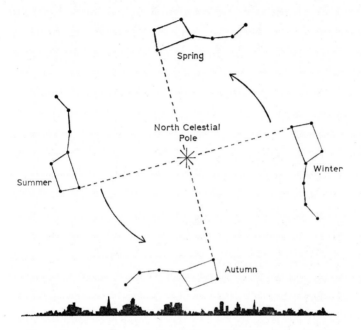

FIG. 3. Seasonal changes in the position of the Plough at midnight

right through the year. But as they wheel about the north celestial pole, as if tied to it by invisible strings, they occupy different places in the sky both during a night and during a year. At midnight in winter, for instance, The Plough lies to the east of *Polaris*. Six months later, and again at midnight, it lies to the west of that star. At midnight in spring The Plough lies to the south of *Polaris* and has its highest place in our skies. Six months later, and still at midnight, it is low in the north and not in a good position for observation. Knowing this, and if you also know that the time is near midnight, you can make a pretty good guess as to the season and even the month. On the other hand, if you know the season you can get a good idea of the time of night just by checking on the position of The Plough. Try this out for yourself, both indoors with a planisphere (the one made for $51\frac{1}{2}$°N.) and under the stars at night.

At about the same distance on the other side of the North Pole Star, and almost opposite to The Plough, lie five bright stars forming a slightly lop-sided letter W. These are the five bright stars of Cassiopeia. They too are circumpolar for observers living in latitudes 45°N. and higher. When The Plough is high up, therefore, the W of Cassiopeia is low down in the north and *vice versa*.

In the same way, and if you live in Australia or New Zealand, you will see that the stars which form The Southern Cross are circumpolar. At midnight in the southern autumn (which corresponds to spring in the northern hemisphere) The Southern Cross is at its highest in the sky. But six months later it is low down in the south at midnight.

The Plough and the W of Cassiopeia are both star patterns. The stars forming them, however, only appear to form the patterns; they are not grouped together in space as near neighbours. This is an important point. If two stars look close together in the sky it does not necessarily follow that they are together. It may well be that they are at greatly different distances from us and appear close together only because they happen to be in almost the same direction.

The seven stars of The Plough are really part of a far larger figure, The Great Bear. This figure, essentially a product of the imagination and one believed to have originated with the Ancient Greeks, involves many other stars fainter than those of The Plough. Whereas The Plough is a star pattern, The Great Bear is a constellation figure, and the stars in and around the figure are called the stars of the constellation of The Great Bear. There is also the constellation of The Little Bear, based on a little plough and having *Polaris* at the end of its unnaturally long tail. In a similar way the W of Cassiopeia forms a kind of framework for the constellation of Queen Cassiopeia who, in classical times, was usually shown seated on chair.

Those and many other constellation figures are generally thought to be Ancient Greek in origin, but some may be far older. Early peoples thought much of them, and to the point of thinking more of the figures than the stars around them. This practice is shown in the earliest known star globe, believed to date from the fourth century B.C. and now preserved in a museum in Naples (Plate I). The globe is a solid ball of marble about 26 inches across, but while several constellation figures are engraved on it there is not a single star. In a few cases the stars do seem to suggest the figure they are supposed to represent, but most of them are difficult and even impossible to imagine. It seems that early peoples projected their child-like fancies on to the stars, so turning the night sky into a great moving picture book. Up went gods, goddesses, heroes, heroines, sacred animals and even commonplace things, also many stories connecting them, for it all helped to make the sky a friendly place and to make Man feel at one with the Universe.

While star maps and atlases no longer portray the constellation figures, they provide the constellation names, usually in Latin. Astronomers still refer to the stars by these names—by names like Ursa Major (The Great Bear), Ursa Minor (The Little Bear), Cassiopeia and Crux (The Cross), etc., but they don't worry one bit about the actual figures. You will be wise if you do the same, unless, of course, you are interested in Greek mythology or in this particular aspect of the subject. If so, then some of the books listed in the Appendix will assist you on your way. A. P.

Norton in his atlas lists eighty-nine constellations in both hemispheres of the sky, but in the star maps you are just given the names and the boundaries. There are no over-lapping areas and no vacant spaces. Every star has a place in a specific constellation.

In order to identify the stars it is a good plan to start with a few basic star patterns and then to move on to the con-stellations. A planisphere used in conjunction with *Norton's Star Atlas* will provide all the necessary information, and it is good fun on a clear night to find your own way among the stars. Concentrate at first only on bright stars, and as you pick out the patterns learn the names of the stars. The names are unusual in that they are mainly Arabic in origin, although a few are adapted from the Greek. In addition, a bright star has an alternative name formed by a letter of the Greek alphabet followed by the name of the constella-tion. The North Pole Star, for example, is called *Polaris* or α *Ursae Minoris*. The letter α or alpha generally means that the star is the brightest in its constellation, with β or beta the second brightest, γ or gamma the third, δ or delta the fourth and so on through the alphabet. There are, however, exceptions to the rule. To give one case, *Castor* or α *Geminorum* is less bright than *Pollux*, or β *Geminorum*. Notice too that the constellation name must be in the genitive case. *Polaris* is clearly the star Alpha in the con-stellation *of* Ursa Minor.

In the Appendix you will find a list of all the constellations, together with their genitive forms, also a copy of the Greek alphabet and the names of the twenty brightest stars.

Here, also, are a few important star groups and patterns for northern observers to look out for around midnight at three-monthly intervals.

Winter (mid-December)

The seven bright stars of *Orion* (pronounced Orr-i-on) lie over in the south. They form the matchstick figure of a man with the reddish star *Betelgeuse* (pronounced Bet-el-jooz) in his right shoulder and *Rigel* (pronounced Ri-jel) in his left leg. In between a row of three equally spaced stars form his waist.

Betelgeuse along with *Procyon* (pronounced Pro-sy-on) and *Sirius* (pronounced Si-ri-us) form a large triangle called The Winter Triangle. *Sirius* is the brightest star in the night sky.

Above *Procyon* lie *Castor* and *Pollux*, two stars fairly close together, while on the other side of *Orion*, but higher up, is the reddish star *Aldebaran* (pronounced Al-deb-ar-an). *Aldebaran* has several fainter stars nearby which form a group or, better, cluster of stars known as the *Hyades* (pronounced Hy-a-dees). Also near *Aldebaran* are the *Pleiades* (pronounced Ply-ad-ees), a delightful cluster of stars which looks like a miniature plough.

Almost overhead is *Capella* (pronounced Ca-pel-la), the brightest star in the constellation of Auriga.

Spring (mid-March)

Orion has moved over to the west and *Capella* is low in the north-west. In the south is a sickle-shaped curve of stars. They belong to the constellation of Leo, The Lion. The bright star at the base of The Sickle is *Regulus*, or *Alpha Leonis*.

The Plough is now high up in the sky. Follow along the curve of its handle and you will arrive at *Arcturus* (pronounced Ark-tu-rus) and then at *Spica* (pronounced Spy-ka).

Summer (mid-June)

Regulus in The Sickle has moved over to the west. The bright star almost overhead is *Vega* (pronounced Vee-ga). To the north-east of *Vega* is *Deneb* (pronounced Den-eb) and to the south-east is *Altair* (pronounced Al-tair). These three stars form a large triangle called The Summer Triangle.

Deneb is the head star of five stars which form The Northern Cross. The Cross lies in the Milky Way, with its longer axis or arm lying along the Milky Way.

Autumn (mid-September)

The Summer Triangle has moved over to the west and Orion is just appearing in the east. In the south are four stars forming The Square of Pegasus. Only three of these stars, however, belong to the constellation of Pegasus. *Alpheratz*, the upper-left star, is *Alpha Andromedae*.

If you start with these stars and patterns it will be an easy matter to trace out others and to get to know the names and places of quite a large number of stars. While doing this bear in mind three important items of geometry connected with the celestial sphere.

1. *The celestial meridian*, or imaginary line which runs through the zenith (or point directly overhead) and the north and south points. The celestial pole lies on this line. If you live, say, in London, latitude $51\frac{1}{2}°$N., the north celestial pole is $51\frac{1}{2}°$ above the north point measured along the celestial meridian. This, of course, is the approximate height or altitude of *Polaris* above the northern horizon.

2. *The celestial equator*, or imaginary line which circles the celestial sphere midway between the north and south celestial poles. It is a *great circle* in that it divides the celestial sphere into two equal halves. In the sky it forms an imaginary arch based on the east and west points. If you live north of the equator the arch is in the southern part of the sky, and *vice versa*. The celestial equator reaches its greatest height where it crosses the celestial meridian. Its height is then 90° minus the latitude. If you live in London, therefore, it reaches a height of $38\frac{1}{2}°$ above the southern horizon. The celestial equator passes near the bright stars *Altair*; *Procyon*; *Delta Orionis* (the most easterly star of the three in Orion's waist or belt); *Alpha Ceti*; and runs about midway between *Regulus* and *Spica*. These stars and

all others similarly placed therefore rise almost due east and set almost due west.

3. *The ecliptic*, or apparent path of the Sun among the stars. As we have already seen, it is inclined at an angle of $23\frac{1}{2}°$ to the celestial equator, which it crosses at two points, the vernal equinox, or First Point of Aries, and the autumnal equinox. More important for us at this stage, however, is the fact that the ecliptic passes through twelve constellations which together form a comparatively narrow belt or zone in the sky called the *zodiac*. The Sun, Moon and planets are always found in the zodiac, and it is therefore important to know just where it lies at any time. The twelve constellations are: Aries (The Ram), Taurus (The Bull), Gemini (The Twins), Cancer (The Crab), Leo (The Lion), Virgo (The Virgin), Libra (The Scales), Scorpius (The Scorpion), Sagittarius (The Archer), Capricornus (The Capricorn), Aquarius (The Water Carrier) and Pisces (The Fishes).

The ecliptic itself passes near the bright stars *Alpha Arietis*, *Aldebaran*, *Pollux*, *Regulus*, *Spica* and *Antares* (pronounced An-tar-ez).

Although every star has a place in a constellation, it is necessary in astronomy to fix that position on the celestial sphere with the greatest possible accuracy. This is done by using a co-ordinate framework based on *Right Ascension* (R.A.) and *Declination* (Decl.). This works in a way similar to longitude and latitude on the Earth. R.A. corresponds to longitude, while Decl. corresponds to latitude. Just as longitude is measured from a particular place (the meridian passing through the old Royal Observatory at Greenwich), so R.A. is measured from the First Point of Aries, but working *eastwards* all the time.

The trouble with this sytem is that the First Point of Aries is a moving point. Owing to the precession of the equinoxes (which, as we saw, arises from the slow wobble of the Earth as it spins) the First Point of Aries moves westward along the celestial equator at the rate of 50·26 seconds of arc a year. Hence in a century it moves about $1\frac{1}{3}°$ to bring about a serious increase in the R.A.s and Decl.s of all the stars. For this reason astronomers who prepare lists of star positions or atlases always give the epoch or time for which those positions hold good. Corrections for both R.A. and Decl. can then be made if star positions for some other epoch are required. *Norton's Star Atlas* is arranged for the new standard epoch 1950·0.

At present the First Point of Aries lies not in the constellation of Aries but in neighbouring Pisces, and near the border between Pisces and Aquarius. Look for its position among the stars in *Norton's Star Atlas* and try to locate it in the sky: it lies almost directly below *Alpha Andromedae* and *Gamma Pegasi*, the two stars forming the east side of The Square of Pegasus.

The R.A.s of stars are usually given in hours, minutes and seconds of time. There are 24 hours corresponding to 360°, so that each hour is equivalent to 15°, each minute to 15′ (or 15 minutes of arc), and each second to 15″ (or 15 seconds of arc). R.A.oh is therefore the same as R.A.24h.

Declination, like latitude on the Earth, is measured in degrees, minutes and seconds of arc north and south of the equator; in this case, the *celestial* equator. A star like *Capella*, therefore, which lies about half-way between the celestial equator and the north celestial pole, is about +46° in Decl. *Sirius*, on the other hand, is south of the celestial equator, so its Decl. is given as −17° (approximately). The R.A.s and Decl.s of the twenty brightest stars are given in the Appendix. Once you get used to this method of locating stars you can use it for finding other things, like faint comets, planets or star clusters, provided, of course, you know their R.A.s and Decl.s beforehand.

Finally, but by no means least in importance, we must get to know the way astronomers classify the brightnesses of the stars. This is straightforward enough, but at first sight

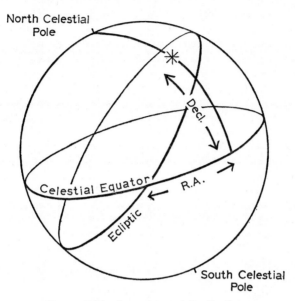

FIG. 4. Right Ascension and Declination

it may seem a little odd. The stars from the brightest to those just visible to the naked eye are graded into six classes or *magnitudes*. The brightest stars are 1st magnitude stars, the faintest are 6th magnitude. A low magnitude number therefore means a bright star, while a high number like 22 or 23 means that the star is extremely faint—so faint, in fact, that it can only just be photographed with the 200-inch Palomar telescope, the largest telescope in the world. A 1st mag. star is about $2\frac{1}{2}$ times brighter than one of the 2nd mag. and 100 times brighter than one of the 6th mag. A 2nd mag. star is $2\frac{1}{2}$ times brighter than one of the 3rd mag., a 3rd mag. is $2\frac{1}{2}$ times brighter than one of the 4th mag. and so on.

Our remark that the brightest stars are 1st magnitude was,

29

however, rather wide of the truth. These stars have quite a range in magnitude and to cope with this astronomers have extended the magnitude scale from 1 to 0 through to −1 and −2. Hence *Sirius* is of mag. −1·47, *Capella* is of mag. 0·09, and *Spica* is of mag. 0·98. Nor are the faintest stars visible on a clear night all of mag. 6. They may range from 5 to 7, according to the brightness of the stars themselves and on the degree of clearness of the sky. What Londoners would call a clear night Africans might well call a poor night. Another factor is the goodness of the eyesight of the observer. Some people who see well during the day see less clearly in the dark, not because it is dark but because their eyes work less efficiently in semi-light. Even if your eyesight is good never leave a well-lit room expecting to see faint stars: the eyes have to grow accustomed to the darkness or, as we say in scientific terms, they have to become dark-adapted. The eyes are not fully dark-adapted until you have spent at least twenty minutes in the dark, so you should wait at least that period of time before searching for faint objects in the sky.

3

The Sun

OF ALL the stars, the Sun is by far the brightest, and, it might be thought, the largest. It comes as a surprise to most people to hear that the Sun, as a star, is a very ordinary fellow, and to the point of being a bit of a dwarf. As we shall see later, there are stars millions of times larger than the Sun and many thousands of times more *luminous*, or intrinsically bright. On the other hand, and in all fairness to the Sun, we must realize that there are stars which are both far smaller and several thousand times less luminous.

The Sun's diameter is 864,000 miles, or well over one hundred times the diameter of the Earth. This means that more than a million Earths could be packed inside the Sun. If we represent the Earth by a tennis ball then the Sun would be a globe 22 feet across placed about half a mile away. The $\frac{1}{2}$ mile corresponds to the Sun's distance of nearly 93,000,000 miles. This is a distance so great that if, like the little Soviet space station, Lunik 2, we could reach the Moon in $1\frac{1}{2}$ days, a journey to the Sun at that rate of travel would take about $1\frac{1}{2}$ years.

Although the Sun is so large, it is so far away as to occupy quite a tiny part of the sky. Its average apparent diameter is only about 32′, or just over $\frac{1}{2}$°, which means that it would not even cover the Pleiades. A halfpenny held about 9 feet from the eye has just about the same apparent size as the Sun. Yet this apparent size is not constant: it is largest (32′ 35″) about January 3rd and least

(31′ 31″) about July 4th. The reason for the change lies in the fact that the Earth travels round the Sun in a slightly oval-shaped or *elliptical* path. It is accordingly almost 6,000,000 miles nearer to the Sun in early January than it is in early July. This variation in distance is immense by Earthly standards but quite small in relation to the average distance of just under 93,000,000 miles. In brief, although the Earth's path or orbit is an ellipse, the departure of that ellipse from a circle is comparatively small.

The Sun's ever-changing distance during a year has no bearing whatever on the seasons. The warmth of summer arises from the fact that the midday Sun is fairly high in the sky (62° for London). His rays of light and heat therefore meet the Earth's surface at a fairly steep angle and can warm the ground quite effectively. In addition, the summer Sun spends longer in the sky than does the winter Sun, which again helps considerably on the heat credit side. In winter the Sun's noon height is quite low (15° for London). His rays then pass through a great thickness of air and are robbed of much of their heating power. They also meet the Earth's surface at a fairly low angle and so warm the ground far less effectively than when the Sun rides high.

Mention of the Sun's apparent size reminds us that he sometimes looks above normal size at sunrise and sunset. At such times he can have a slightly oval or squashed look and also a decided reddish colour. The increased size is an optical illusion believed to be due to our seeing the Sun along with familiar objects on the skyline. He is then no larger than when overhead. The slightly oval appearance is due to the Earth's atmosphere. As sunlight or any other light travels through the air it is bent or *refracted*. Over short distances the amount of bending or refraction is very small, but its effects become noticeable when the Sun is near the horizon. Light from the Sun's upper *limb* or edge then travels through a great thickness of air, but light from points lower down travels through an even greater thickness

Plate 1. The Farnese Celestial Globe (National Museum, Naples)

Plate 2. The London Planetarium. Night sky showing the constellation figure of Cygnus, The Swan, the Celestial Equator (divided into hours), the Celestial Meridian (broken line, divided into degrees) and the Ecliptic (broken line, divided into days)

and therefore undergoes greater refraction. The net result is that the Sun's disk as a whole is displaced vertically upwards by about $\frac{1}{2}°$, but with the lower limb displaced approximately 5' more than the upper. So, although the Sun has set, at least in theory, it is forced to linger for a few extra minutes above the horizon and to assume an oval shape. The same effects can be noticed at sunrise, and for the same reason.

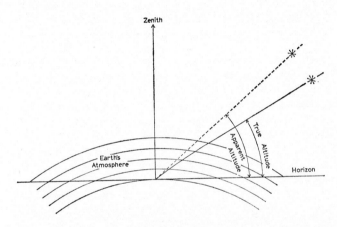

FIG. 5. Atmospheric refraction

Atmospheric refraction is nil for objects at the zenith but gradually increases away from the zenith to reach a maximum of about 33' at the horizon. This means that the Sun and all objects in the night sky are shifted slightly upwards from their true positions.

The reddish colour of a rising or setting Sun is also due to the Earth's atmosphere. This not only refracts sunlight but scatters it as well. The scattering is done by air molecules and dust particles which scatter the blue rays in sunlight more than the rest and so produce a blue sky. This process

C

is most effective when the Sun or Moon are low down in the sky: quite often only the orange and red rays get through to the observer without being scattered. From a position in space, free from the Earth's mantle of air, the sky would look quite black. Even at a height of 150 miles, and as Major Gagarin found when he made his historic flight around the Earth, the sky is black and the stars can be seen shining along with the Sun.

If the Earth travelled round the Sun with uniform speed in a circular path or orbit, keeping time by the Sun would be a fairly easy matter. It would be even easier if the Earth's equator coincided with the plane of its orbit, for the Sun would then move along the celestial equator at the rate of nearly 1° a day. Every day at 6 a.m. it would rise due east, at 12 p.m. or noon stand on the celestial meridian, and at 6 p.m. set due west. Sundials would be easy to make and could be relied on to give the correct time all through the year.

Unfortunately for this point of view, the Sun travels along the ecliptic, or in a path inclined at about $23\frac{1}{2}$° to the celestial equator. Furthermore, his motion is by no means uniform, being faster than average in early January and slower than average in early July. This variable speed is just a reflection of the Earth's motion in its elliptical orbit. According to Kepler's second law of planetary motion, a planet moves in its orbit so that an imaginary line connecting it with the Sun sweeps over equal areas in equal intervals of time. To obey this law the Earth moves faster when it is at *perihelion* (or nearest the Sun) about January 3rd than when it is at *aphelion* (or furthest from the Sun) about July 4th.

This behaviour of the Sun complicates time-reckoning by the Sun. It also explains why a sundial only seldom gives the right time, for clocks are designed to operate at a perfectly uniform rate. To obtain clock-time from a sundial it is necessary to subtract a quantity known as the *equation of time*. This constantly changing quantity can be positive or negative, and in the course of a year reaches four maximum values:

1. −14 m. 21 s. on or about February 12th.
2. +3 m. 45 s. on or about May 15th.
3. −6 m. 22 s. on or about July 27th.
4. +16 m. 22 s. on or about November 3rd.

In between these dates, about April 16th, June 14th, September 1st and December 25th, the equation of time is zero. About these four dates, but only about these dates, the sundial registers clock-time.

On what object, then, is clock-time based? Certainly not on the *apparent Sun*, or the Sun which we can see, but on a mean Sun which is not really a Sun at all. The mean Sun is simply a point which is imagined to move along the celestial equator at the average rate of the apparent Sun. This explains in part the expression G.M.T. (Greenwich Mean Time), or time based on a mean Sun. In practice, however, observatory clocks are checked not against the mean Sun, which cannot be observed anyway, and certainly not against the apparent Sun, but more easily and accurately against the stars.

The determination of time and maintenance of a time service are important activities at some major observatories. The principles underlying them, however, are complicated and their understanding requires a sound knowledge of practical astronomy. Two of the few books which give good coverage to this subject are given in the Bibliography, but the basic ideas are usually discussed in most textbooks of astronomy. You will find that there are all sorts of time: sidereal, apparent solar, mean solar, astronomical mean solar, universal, ephemeris, civil, local and standard, also that there are different sorts of year: tropical, solar, anomalistic, synodic and civil. Time for the philosopher may be an ever-rolling stream but to the astronomer its significance undoubtedly lies in the way it is measured.

About a year ago we made the Sun the main actor in a presentation at The London Planetarium. We called the presentation 'The Land of the Midnight Sun' and demonstrated the Sun's apparent motion as seen from different latitudes about mid-June. It proved most popular with the general public but revealed a profound ignorance on the part of many visitors. They had, it appeared, become so used to the Sun's pattern of behaviour as seen from their own locality that they just could not believe that it could be any different elsewhere.

You can always safely predict the Sun's apparent movement for a particular place and time once you know (a) the latitude of the place, (b) the Sun's declination, or angular distance north or south of the celestial equator. To obtain the declination you will need an *ephemeris*, or book or astronomical tables. Professional astronomers and navigators use *The Astronomical Ephemeris*. This is published annually by H.M. Stationery Office, and, among other things, tabulates the R.A. and Decl. of the apparent Sun for every day of the year. The R.A. is given to a fraction of a second of time, the Decl. is given to a fraction of a second of arc. The tables also give the Sun's apparent semi-diameter and the equation of time for every day in the year. Similar daily information is also given in *Whitaker's Almanack*, where the Sun's Decl. is given to minutes of arc and his R.A. to seconds of time.

Knowing then the latitude and the Sun's Decl., our task is to find the Sun's noon altitude, or his height above the horizon when he is on the meridian. The latitude enables us straightway to fix the position of the celestial equator, for the latter crosses the meridian at a height of 90° —latitude. We then have only to add the declination (and taking due regard of its sign + or −) to fix the Sun's position.

One can, of course, make good progress in this matter merely by knowing the Sun's Decl. on the following four dates:

March 21st, vernal equinox, Decl. 0°.
June 21st, summer solstice, Decl. +23° 26′.
September 23rd, autumnal equinox, Decl. 0°.
December 22nd, winter solstice, Decl. −23° 26′.

These dates vary a little from year to year, but they are precise enough for our purposes. We can also regard the Sun's maximum declination north or south as $23\frac{1}{2}°$.

With these figures at hand, and bearing in mind what has already been stated in Chapter 1, consider the following five cases:

1. *North Pole.* Latitude 90°N. The celestial equator is on the horizon. Daytime lasts from about March 21st to September 23rd, with the Sun reaching a greatest height of only $23\frac{1}{2}°$ near June 21st. On March 21st and September 23rd the Sun is theoretically half above and half below the horizon, but atmospheric refraction causes the entire disk to be seen. He then appears to roll once round the skyline in 24 hours. Night lasts from September 23rd to March 21st, but for about 8 weeks the Sun is so little below the horizon as to provide a substantial semi-light or twilight glow.

2. *Arctic Circle.* Latitude $66\frac{1}{2}°$N. The celestial equator runs across the southern part of the sky to intersect the celestial meridian at an altitude of $23\frac{1}{2}°$. On December 22nd, therefore, the Sun reaches the horizon at midday to give a daytime of only a few minutes. Six months later his greatest altitude at midday is 47°, so that at midnight on June 21st he is still in view, but on the northern horizon. Daytime lasts 24 hours. At Hammerfest in Norway, for example, latitude about $71\frac{1}{2}°$N., the Sun shines continuously over several weeks before and after June 21st. In compensation he is absent for several weeks around December 22nd.

3. *Equator.* Latitude 0°. The Sun passes through the zenith on March 21st and September 23rd. Between March 21st and September 23rd he moves into the northern part of the sky, to reach on June 21st an altitude of $66\frac{1}{2}°$ above

the northern horizon. Between September 23rd and March 21st he moves into the southern part of the sky, to reach on December 22nd an altitude of $66\frac{1}{2}°$ above the southern horizon. Throughout the year he rises straight upwards and sets straight downwards, thereby giving a short twilight time.

4. *Antarctic circle*. Latitude $66\frac{1}{2}°$S. The pattern of the Sun's behaviour is similar to that at the Arctic Circle, but for 'southern' read 'northern' and for 'December 22nd' read 'June 21st' and *vice versa.*

5. *South Pole*. Latitude 90°S. The pattern of the Sun's behaviour is similar to that at the North Pole, but with daytime from September 23rd to March 21st and night from March 21st to September 23rd.

The Sun is never so much an object of general interest as when he is totally eclipsed by the Moon. On these occasions the Moon's dark body covers the Sun's bright face and so cuts off by far the greater part of his light. It is one of those curious accidents in nature that the two bodies should at times subtend the same angle and so make possible a total solar eclipse. During totality the sky no longer looks blue but almost black, the brighter stars and planets can be seen, and a *corona* or halo of pearly white light surrounds the Moon. The comparatively faint coronal light bathes the countryside in an eerie glow which makes the event even more sublime and awe-inspiring.

If the Earth, Moon and Sun kept always in the same plane there would be an eclipse of the Sun every month at the time of new Moon. It so happens that the plane of the Moon's path or orbit is inclined to the Earth's at an angle of about 5°. At the time of new Moon, therefore, the Moon usually passes above or below the Sun and no eclipse takes place.

For a total eclipse of the Sun by the Moon the Moon's shadow cone must reach the Earth to form a shadow patch on the Earth's surface. But since the Moon is a moving body its shadow clearly trails over the Earth's surface, and in a west-to-east direction. The observer must therefore be in the path or track of the shadow patch if he is to see the Sun totally eclipsed. This path cannot be more than about 170 miles wide but it can be thousands of miles long.

The duration of a total solar eclipse at any place in the path depends on the speed of the shadow patch across the observer who, incidentally, is being carried around from

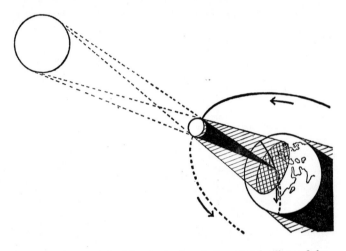

FIG. 6. Track of the Moon's shadow during a total eclipse of the Sun

west to east on the rotating Earth. If he is latitude 45° his rate of travel is about 735 miles an hour: if at the equator the rate is 1,040 miles an hour. The shadow itself moves in space at about 2,100 miles an hour, so its speed over an observer in latitude 45° is 2,100 − 735 or 1,365 miles an hour, and over one at the equator 2,100 − 1,040 or 1,060 miles an hour. The average duration of a total solar eclipse is about 3 minutes, but under the most favourable circumstances it can be nearly 8 minutes.

If for any reason the observer is situated outside the shadow track, even to the point of being some 2,000 to 3,000 miles away, he will see the Sun only partly or partially eclipsed. You will appreciate from this that the chances of seeing a partial eclipse are far greater than those of seeing a total one. Even so, the chances of seeing anything at all depend in the last analysis on the weather. All too often have astronomers travelled great distances to set up their telescopes in an eclipse track, only to see a blanket of cloud during the precious minutes of totality. Again, the tip of the Moon's shadow cone may fall short of the Earth's surface. When this happens the Moon looks smaller than the Sun and at the time of greatest eclipse leaves a ring or annulus of light. Eclipses of this kind are termed *annular* eclipses.

How often do eclipses of the Sun occur? For reasons given in most books on elementary astronomy, eclipses of the Sun and Moon are repeated in the same order every 18 years $10\frac{1}{3}$ days (if 5 leap years intervene) or 18 years $11\frac{1}{3}$ days (if 4 leap years intervene). This period, known to the Chaldeans in the second century B.C., is called the *saros*. The total solar eclipse of February 25th, 1952, can therefore be regarded as a return of the one of February 14th, 1934. Similarly, there will be another on March 7th, 1970. The eclipse track, however, does not fall over the same places each time, but on the average passes over the same place only once in 360 years. There are also several other eclipse cycles, all of which along with the saros enable astronomers to predict eclipses not just years but centuries ahead. A study of these cycles and of past records shows that in any one year there can be as many as four eclipses of the Sun or as few as two.

The standard reference work on eclipses is *Canon der Finsternisse* by T. R. von Oppolzer, published in Vienna in 1887 and now very rare. It gives 8,000 solar eclipses between 1207 B.C. and A.D. 2161 along with maps showing the shadow tracks of all total and annular eclipses north of latitude 30°S. It also gives 5,200 eclipses of the Moon for the same period.

For information about the eclipses in a coming year you should consult *The Astronomical Ephemeris* and *Whitaker's Almanack* for that year, also the annual *Handbook of the British Astronomical Association*.

The next total solar eclipse visible from the British Isles will not occur until August 11th, 1999, to be followed by one on September 23rd, 2090.

The pearly light of the corona seen during a total solar eclipse (Plate 3) belongs to the Sun. It tells us that what we normally see of the Sun is just its main body—that surrounding the body lies an extremely deep atmosphere of hot gases. Photographs of the corona during totality often reveal a wealth of detail and delicate tracery in its structure. They also show that the corona can extend millions of miles from the Sun's body. Even so, it appears to be just the lower part of a solar atmosphere which, in an extremely rarefied form, reaches right out to the Earth and even beyond. The exploration of interplanetary space by space probes shows that charged electrified particles of many kinds reach the Earth and the region around it from the Sun. There are also good reasons for thinking that the Sun is surrounded by an extensive layer of dust which is revealed in part by its reflected light—the *zodiacal light*.

Have you ever seen the zodiacal light? It is a cone-shaped band of diffuse light which can sometimes be seen just after sunset or just before sunrise. The base of the cone lies on the horizon while its axis slopes upwards along the ecliptic. It is not usually conspicuous, but when conditions are favourable it can be quite spectacular. I first saw it in my youth back in the 1930s. The sky was remarkably clear, the Sun had set and over in the west the zodiacal light stretched obliquely upwards, broad and bright in the already darkened sky. I met it on reaching the brow of a busy bridge, stopped and stared in astonishment, and felt impelled to point it out to others. But I said not a word: the passers-by hurried on, so intent upon the business of life as to discourage any further attempts at communication.

The zodiacal light is most likely to be seen after sunset in spring or before sunrise in autumn. The Moon must be absent and the air clear. On occasion it has been traced right across the sky, which supports the notion that it is not only centred on the Sun but extends outwards all around, in and near the plane of the Earth's orbit.

If you observe a total eclipse of the Sun through a small telescope or pair of binoculars you stand a good chance of seeing the solar prominences. These look like pink flames but in reality are surging masses of intensely hot hydrogen gas which on occasion may rise for over 100,000 miles above the Sun's body. But by far the most important eruptive feature of the Sun's body is the flares, for they have immediate effects on the Earth. They emit intense bursts of ultra-violet and X-ray radiation which travel to the Earth in just over 8 minutes and cause short-wave radio fade-outs. In addition they blow out streams of electrified particles which reach the Earth some 20 to 40 hours later and cause magnetic storms. They cause the thin upper air to glow, thereby giving rise to the beautiful coloured lights of the *aurorae* or *polar lights*. Flares also emit bursts of cosmic rays, or charged atomic particles of high energy which travel at a speed approaching that of light.

Aurorae are best seen in the far north and south, or in regions fairly near the Earth's north and south magnetic poles. They take many forms, appearing perhaps as quivering fingers of light, as beautiful curtains and draperies hanging in the sky or as diffuse reddish clouds. They can be seen from southern England and even further south, but in built-up areas even an intense display can escape general notice—such are the rival effects of street lighting, industrial haze and the background sky glow.

Another interesting feature of the Sun is sunspots (Plates 4 and 5). These look like black spots on the Sun's bright face. Very large ones are naked-eye objects: they are usually noticed by members of the general public when the Sun is low down and robbed of most of his normal brilliance. The Sun is, however, seldom completely free from spots, which, incidentally, are not black at all. They are really quite hot but appear dark by contrast with their even hotter surroundings.

If you have a small telescope don't be content to read about sunspots in a book. See them for yourself and record their changing positions. But on no account look through the telescope at the Sun. A telescope not only magnifies the Sun but acts as a very effective burning-glass. You would seriously damage the eye and stand every chance of doing so even if you placed a piece of smoked glass behind the eyepiece. In any case the smoked glass would probably crack or splinter, adding still further to the damage. The safe way is to place a piece of white card behind the telescope. The Sun's magnified image can then be formed by projection on the card. The spots will stand out quite clearly and their positions in relation to the Sun's disk can then be plotted in safety on the card with a pencil.

If you have a good telescope and would like to use it on the regular recording of sunspots you should become a member of the British Astronomical Association (B.A.A.). The Association has a section specially devoted to solar observation and this kind of work. You will then get all the necessary advice as to the correct procedures and will have the satisfaction of contributing to the sum total of scientific knowledge. The B.A.A. also has a section for the observation of aurorae and the zodiacal light, but here again you cannot join the section until you have been elected a member of the Association. In any case, don't join the B.A.A. just for the sake of joining something. Make sure first that you are more than mildly interested in astronomy.

4

The Moon

THE Moon, at an average distance of 238,800 miles from the Earth, is our nearest neighbour in space. It is also the Earth's only natural satellite, and a large one in comparison with its primary. Its diameter is 2,160 miles, that of the Earth being nearly 8,000 miles. If, then, we represent the Earth by a tennis ball, the Moon on that scale will be about the size of a marble placed 6 feet away. If you are impressed by the launching of artificial satellites in recent years, don't forget the Moon. Consider its size and distance, also the fact that it was 'launched' probably 4,000,000,000 years ago—and is still going strong!

You will find the Moon interesting in at least three ways: (1) by its behaviour as a naked-eye object throughout the year, (2) by its appearance as seen through a telescope and (3) by its value as a space station in the future.

Like the Sun, the Moon not only shares in the general rotation of the celestial sphere but also travels in a general west-to-east direction against the background of stars. It does so because we view it from the rotating Earth and because it travels around the Earth once in about a month in a general west-to-east direction. In a day it therefore moves through about 12°, and in an hour through about $\frac{1}{2}$°, or its own apparent diameter. This means that its average speed in its path or orbit is over 2,000 miles an hour (2,300 m.p.h., to be more precise). You can easily check this movement for yourself. If the Moon lies close to a bright star like *Spica* or *Regulus* notice its change in position after an hour or two. You will find that relative to that star it has moved to a more easterly position.

The Moon shines by reflecting the Sun's light. As it travels around the Earth we therefore see different parts of its sunlit side. This gives rise to apparent changes in its form or shape, or, as we say in astronomy, to the monthly *phase cycle*. Many people find this difficult to understand. At least they appreciate that there must be phases but cannot account for a particular phase at a particular time. Only too often have artists drawn or painted a sky with the Moon the wrong way round or having the wrong phase for its position.

Let's consider, then, the change in the Moon's appearance and position at weekly intervals from one new Moon to the next.

1. *New Moon.* The Moon lies in the direction of the Sun and is missing from the sky. It is usually above or below the Sun, but if directly in line, gives rise to a total or annular eclipse of the Sun. As it moves away from this position we see it first as a thin crescent which grows or *waxes* as more and more of the sunlit side can be seen from the Earth. The bow of the crescent always points towards the Sun while the crescent ends or *horns* point away from the Sun.

2. *First Quarter.* In 7 days the Moon has travelled one-quarter of one total journey from new Moon to new Moon. The angle Sun-Earth-Moon is 90°: we therefore see a half-Moon, or one-half of the Moon's sunlit side. A half-Moon on March 21st and September 23rd is on the celestial meridian at sunset. In winter it lies to the east of the meridian at sunset, in summer it lies to the west of the meridian at sunset. As it moves away from first quarter the Moon grows into a hunch-backed or *gibbous* form (Plate 6).

3. *Full Moon.* The Moon lies in a direction opposite to that of the Sun. If directly in line it will be in the Earth's shadow and undergo an eclipse. Usually it lies outside the

Earth's shadow cone, with all its sunlit face turned towards us. It is on the celestial meridian at midnight. The full Moon on March 21st and September 23rd (and ignoring the effects of atmospheric refraction) rises in the east as the Sun sets in the west. As it moves away from the position of full, the Moon decreases or *wanes* through a gibbous form.

4. *Last Quarter*. In 21 days the Moon has travelled three-quarters of one total journey from new Moon to new Moon. The angle Sun-Earth-Moon is again 90°, or 270° if we continue to reckon anti-clockwise. We therefore see a half-Moon, or one-half of the Moon's sunlit side. The last-quarter-Moon on March 21st and September 23rd is on the celestial meridian at sunrise. In winter it lies to the west of the meridian, in summer it lies to the east of the meridian.

5. *New Moon*. As the Moon moves towards the Sun the crescent form wanes until lost in the Sun's bright light. Two or three days before New Moon the Moon lies low in the eastern sky just before sunrise, with the horns of the crescent pointing away from the Sun.

You should, of course, take none of this for granted but wherever possible check it for yourself by referring to the Moon in the sky. In the same way you should become familiar with the changes in the Moon's meridian height throughout the year.

This further item involves a consideration of the Moon's Decl. As we saw in the previous chapter, the plane of the Moon's orbit is inclined at 5° (5° 8' more precisely) to the plane of the ecliptic. Its Decl. therefore varies between the limits $23\frac{1}{2}° + 5°$, or $28\frac{1}{2}°$, and $- 23\frac{1}{2}° - 5°$, or $- 28\frac{1}{2}°$. Its path must clearly cross the ecliptic at two points. The one where it passes from below to above the ecliptic, that is, with Decl. increasing, is called the *ascending node*. The one where it passes from above to below the ecliptic, that is, with Decl. decreasing, is called the *descending node*. The nodes are not fixed points. As a pair they *retrograde*, or travel round the ecliptic in an east-to-west direction once in a little under 19 years. This clearly complicates the issue as regards predicting the Moon's position, but fortunately tables of its R.A. and Decl. each day are readily available.

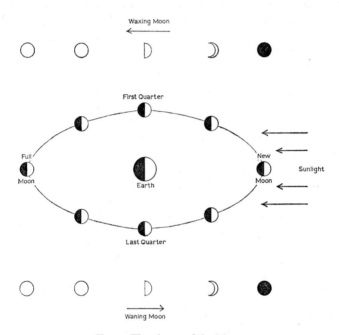

FIG. 7. The phases of the Moon

The information (along with the times of moonrise and moonset) is provided in *Whitaker's Almanack*, and to greater precision in *The Astronomical Ephemeris*.

During the summer months (June, July, August) the Sun rides high in the sky at midday. Hence at midnight the ecliptic crosses the celestial meridian low in the south. The full and near-full Moons therefore appear low in the sky. If the Moon is full on June 21, its altitude at midnight as seen from London will be as little as $15° - 5°$, or $10°$, and no more than $15° + 5°$, or $20°$.

During the winter months (November, December, January) the Sun rides low in the sky at midday. Hence at midnight the ecliptic crosses the celestial meridian high in

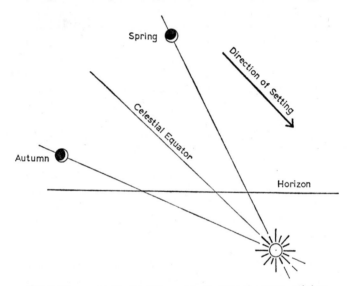

FIG. 8. The reason for the difference in the Moon's aspect and time of setting in spring and autumn

the south. The full Moon and near-full Moons therefore appear high in the sky. If the Moon is full on December 22nd its altitude at midnight as seen from London will be as much as $61\frac{1}{2}° + 5°$, or $66\frac{1}{2}°$, and no less than $61\frac{1}{2}° - 5°$, or $56\frac{1}{2}°$.

Around March 21st and September 23rd, when the Sun is on or near the celestial equator, the full Moon also lies on or near the equator. It therefore rises almost due east

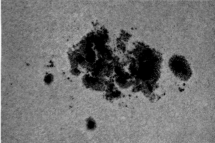

Plate 3. Total eclipse of the Sun (Lick Observatory)

Plate 4. Large group of Sunspots, May 17th, 1951 (Mount Wilson and Palomar Observatories)

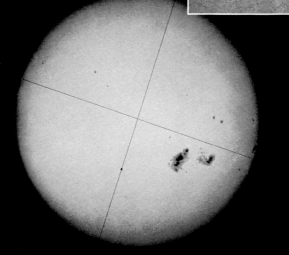

Plate 5. The Giant Sunspot of April 9th, 1947 (Royal Observatory, Cape of Good Hope)

Plate 6.
The Moon, age 10 days
(Lick Observatory)

Plate 7.
Mars, Jupiter, Saturn
and Pluto (Mount
Wilson and Palomar
Observatories)

MARS

JUPITER

SATURN

PLUTO

and sets almost due west to reach a meridian altitude of $38\frac{1}{2}° + 5°$, or $43\frac{1}{2}°$, at most, and $38\frac{1}{2}° - 5°$, or $33\frac{1}{2}°$, at least.

A glance at the tables of the Moon's Decl. shows that its daily change in Decl. is quite considerable. This has a great influence on its times of rising and setting, and bears directly on the phenomenon of the *Harvest Moon*.

The Harvest Moon is the full Moon which occurs nearest the autumnal equinox. In this position the Decl. is changing at a minimum rate, which in turn reduces the intervals between successive moonrises to a minimum. In practical terms, the Harvest Moon rises later each day by little more than 20 minutes, whereas usually the Moon rises later each day by about 50 minutes. It therefore acts as a most effective light-giver in September and October, and to observers in mid-northerly latitudes gives the impression of being brighter than usual. The effect is most noticeable when the ascending node of the Moon's orbit is at or near the First Point of Aries. This happened in 1932 and 1950 and recurs at intervals of nearly 19 years.

On the other hand, and in compensation for this harvest-time boon, the full Moon nearest the time of the vernal equinox can rise later each day by as much as 90 minutes. If this full Moon falls on or next following the vernal equinox, the Sunday after is Easter Day. Should the full Moon fall on a Sunday, Easter Day is the next Sunday after. This fixing of Easter by the Moon was arranged as early as the year 325 by the General Council of Nicaea.

When the Moon is full, and at or near its ascending or descending node, we can expect to see a total eclipse of the Moon. The Sun, Earth and Moon are then almost in one and the same straight line. Eclipses of the Moon are rarer than solar ones, but they can be seen from over a large area of the Earth's surface. Information about them, as for solar eclipses, is provided annually in *The Astronomical Ephemeris*, the *Handbook* of the B.A.A. and *Whitaker's Almanack*.

D

In some years there may be none at all, in others as many as three are possible. Along with those of the Sun they are repeated in very nearly the same order after the saros period of 18 years 11 days.

A total eclipse of the Moon can last about an hour. This is because the cone of the Earth's shadow at the Moon's distance is some $2\frac{1}{2}$ times wider than the Moon itself. The Moon does not necessarily disappear however. On occasions it has been blotted out, but usually it shines with a copperish light. This light is sunlight reddened by its long passage through the Earth's atmosphere and refracted into the Earth's otherwise black shadow. If we could stand on the Moon at the time the Earth would present a wonderful sight. It would more than cover the Sun's body and its atmosphere would be ablaze with fiery red light.

Our statement made earlier that the Moon travels round the Earth once a month now requires further comment. The idea of the calendar month goes back to early times when the Moon was regarded as timekeeper number one. The month was then taken as the interval between one new Moon and the next. This interval, called a *lunation* or *synodic month*, is just over $29\frac{1}{2}$ days. But a *tropical year*, or the period between two successive vernal equinoxes, is nearly $365\frac{1}{4}$ days. Twelve lunations therefore fall short of a year by $11\frac{1}{4}$ days, and to keep the two in step some years were given an extra month, or 13 months altogether. Nowadays we adopt the scheme, first introduced by Julius Caesar, of letting the lunations wander freely through a calendar month of 30 or 31 days, with 28 days for February (29 days in a leap year).

The *sidereal month*, or time taken by the Moon to travel once round the Earth, is about 27 d. 7 h. 43 m. This is its period of revolution relative to the stars. Why the difference of over 2 days between the synodic and sidereal months? The answer lies in the fact that the synodic month is reckoned relative to the Sun, which moves in a west-to-east direction

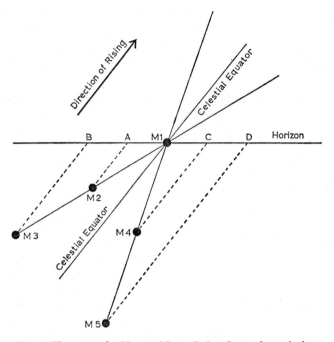

FIG. 9. The reason for Harvest Moon. In late September a day's motion of the Moon carries it from M1 to M2, or from M2 to M3, or only a little further below the horizon. The Moon rises along the lines M2 A and M3 B, or parallel to the celestial equator. In March, however, it rises along the lines M4 C and M5 D and therefore is much more delayed in its rising on successive nights

against the stars. In a synodic month, therefore, the Moon has not only to travel right round the sky but also make good a further 27° in order to catch up with the Sun.

One of my most memorable boyhood experiences was a first view of the Moon through a telescope. The telescope was a poor one, for I made it myself out of two lenses and a cardboard tube. Still, it showed up the great plains or *maria* and many of the craters. If it told me little about the Moon it did at least point the way to a better instrument. The lenses were both single glasses of the magnifying type. The larger and weaker of the two served as the *objective* or *object-glass*. That is, it formed the image to be examined by the eyepiece. It had a focal length of 40 inches, which, with the single-lens eyepiece of 1-inch focal length, provided a magnification of 40. My next telescope was much better. The object-glass was *achromatic*, or free from false colour. It consisted of two lenses, one of crown glass and one of flint glass, mounted so closely together as to appear like a single lens. This instrument also magnified about 40 times but with much sharper and clearer definition. Until recently I worked with a reflecting telescope. In this the image to be examined by the eyepiece is formed by a mirror, or single disk of glass made slightly concave on its front surface. The surface is *aluminized*, or covered by an extremely thin deposit of highly polished aluminium. The diameter of the mirror in my case was 9 inches. The telescope gave wonderful views of the Moon's surface, and on good nights, when the air was clear and steady, could be given magnifications up to 240. Instruments of this size, however, are fairly expensive, and anyone wishing to buy one should first get expert advice.

Achromatic telescopes (or *refractors*) suitable for looking at the Moon and other objects can now be purchased fairly cheaply. Dealers in second-hand instruments usually have a few in stock, but some dealers tend to over-price them irrespective of their optical quality. Small telescopes (below, say, 2 inches in *aperture*, or object-glass diameter) are usually of fairly good optical quality. Some are better than others, while a few are exceptionally good. I once had an old 2-inch telescope made by Jesse Ramsden, a London optician who lived over 100 years ago, which could out-perform most modern telescopes of similar size. I have also looked through a brand-new 3-inch telescope which gave disgracefully bad images; it looked most attractive from the outside but the optics had been just thrown together. Telescopes of 3 inches and more in aperture can be expensive and should always be thoroughly tried out before being purchased. Don't forget that a smart finish outside is no guarantee of good optics inside, also that a telescope is to be looked through rather than looked at. A really good instrument of 2 or 3 inches aperture will take magnifications of 40 to 60 times and give most interesting views of the Moon. Prism binoculars magnifying 20 or 25 times can also be used for the purpose, but in all cases a firm tripod or other steady support is necessary.

You will need a map in order to find your way about on the Moon. Several books on astronomy include a small map which gives the names of the *maria*, or great plains, and of the main walled plains and craters. Otherwise there is *Elger's Map of the Moon*, published in folded form by George Philip and Son Ltd. It was originally drawn by T. Gwyn Elger some years ago but was recently revised by the late Dr. H. P. Wilkins, who added a set of notes on the more interesting features. It is drawn on a scale of about 17 inches to the Moon's diameter, costs only a few shillings and should meet all your requirements.

Dr. Wilkins also prepared a lunar map 300 inches in diameter. This was intended for use by astronomers who make a special study of the Moon's features. It shows thousands of craters and immense numbers of mountain ranges, hills and valleys. It has since been published in book form by Faber and Faber (2nd edn., 1958). The same publishers also reproduce it, with additions, on a scale of 55·4 miles to the inch. This is bound in loose-ring-binder form so that any one sheet can be detached for use directly at the telescope. In addition, there has recently been published a photographic lunar atlas, or collection of photographs of the Moon taken with some of the world's largest telescopes. This was naturally costly to produce and is intended as a work of reference for astronomers. It was prepared under the supervision of Dr. G. P. Kuiper, Director of the Yerkes and McDonald Observatories in the United States, is on the scale 2·5 metres to the Moon's diameter, and shows different regions of the Moon under different angles of illumination.

All these maps and photographs concern only the near part of the Moon. The Moon turns one and the same face towards us, which means that it rotates once on its axis as it travels once round the Earth. Many people find this difficult to follow. I usually tell them to try it out for themselves—to walk once round, say, a chair while always facing the chair. They will then find that they have turned round once, or made one rotation whilst walking once round the chair. Many ask if the far side of the Moon gets any sunshine, and if so, how. They too are advised to walk round a chair, and in daylight.

Actually, we can see not just 50% of the Moon's surface but more nearly 60%. This is because of effects called *librations*. One of them, *libration in latitude*, arises from the fact that the Moon's axis of rotation is not exactly perpendicular to the plane of its orbit. When the axis is tilted towards us we can see $6\frac{1}{2}°$ beyond the Moon's north pole, When the axis is tilted away from us we can see $6\frac{1}{2}°$ beyond the Moon's south pole. Another libration, *libration in longitude*, is due to the fact that the Moon's orbit is an ellipse. Although its rate of rotation is constant, its speed of travel depends on its distance from the Earth. Because of this difference the Moon's revolution does not keep pace with its rotation and we can see about 6° beyond its east and west edges. A third effect is *diurnal libration*. When the Moon is rising we see slightly over its top or western edge, and when it is setting we see slightly over its eastern edge. As a result of all three librations, and in addition to the 41% always seen, a further 18% is alternately seen and not seen. This leaves 41% never seen—at least, by direct means.

What is the far side of the Moon like? We now have a rough idea, thanks to the photographs taken by the Russian space-station, Lunik 3. From these the Russians have been able to build up the first map of the Moon's far side. Lunik 3 did not photograph all the far side, but the information obtained shows that it has fewer *maria* and greater areas of mountains and craters. A copy of the map appeared in the March 1961 issue of the American magazine *Sky and Telescope*. Details about the way the photographs were obtained and used for the map are to be found in *Atlas of the Other Side of the Moon*, published by the U.S.S.R. Academy of Sciences and available in this country.

You may, of course, be quite happy with a few good photographs of the Moon's near side. Copies of these can be obtained from the Royal Astronomical Society. They are of excellent quality and cost only a few shillings each. In any case, don't forget that maps and photographs of the Moon show it inverted or upside-down and also left to right. That is to say, south is at the top and east is on the right. This is how you see the Moon when you observe it through an astronomical telescope. Otherwise, with the naked eye or with a pair of prism binoculars, north is at the top and east is on the left. If you live south of the equator, however, the Moon crosses the celestial meridian in the northern part of the sky. To the eye with or without binoculars it then presents its southern edge uppermost and its eastern edge on the right.

Those who would like to make a special study of the Moon's features should join an amateur body like the Junior Astronomical Society (J.A.S.) or the British Astronomical Association. They will then be able to meet or correspond with experts who will be only too ready and willing to advise them about the choice of a telescope and how to set about observing. They must, however, be seriously keen on the idea and have acquired a sound body of basic knowledge. Astronomers, both amateur and professional, are dedicated to their work and are busy people: they don't suffer fools gladly. The B.A.A. has a Lunar Section under a Director whose job it is to plan, co-ordinate, and evaluate observations. The section also circulates a bulletin, *The Moon*, in which its members share information and compare notes and drawings.

Although the Moon is another world, nearly a quarter of a million miles away, there are still people who believe that it influences the weather, the growth of plants, the balance of the mind and the course of human life. It does none of these things, but it does cause the tides of the seas. Just as the pull of the Earth's gravity reaches to and beyond the Moon, so the pull of the Moon's gravity reaches to the Earth and beyond. The two bodies are held in partnership by these invisible ties to form the Earth-Moon system. This system, in turn, is held captive by the Sun. Hence, it is not the Earth which travels in an elliptical orbit round the Sun but the mass centre, or *centre of gravity*, of the Earth-Moon system. Both the Sun and the Moon by their gravitational pulls distort the waters of the Earth and so produce tides. These are explained in elementary textbooks on astronomy and a knowledge of the principles involved can make a sea-voyage or holiday at the seaside all the more interesting. A little knowledge may be a dangerous thing (as the saying is), but in this connection it can be most satisfying, so long, of course, as you don't set yourself up as an authority or wiseacre.

It's difficult to see how moonlight could affect plants and animals. It is only reflected sunlight, and a fairly feeble light too. The Moon reflects only about 7% of the sunlight that falls upon it, whereas the Earth reflects 39% and the planet Venus reflects as much as 73%. What happens to the remaining 93%? It is absorbed by the Moon's surface and converted into heat, which raises the temperature to about

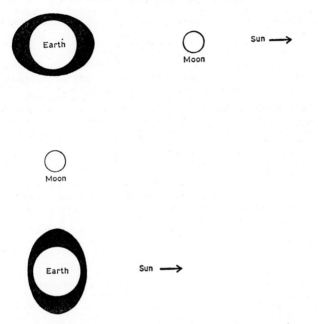

FIG. 10. The Tides. Top: the pulls of the Sun and Moon work together to give the very high 'spring tides'. Bottom: the pulls of the Sun and Moon work against each other to give the much lower 'neap tides'.

100°C. at noon at the equator. Sometimes the Moon shines so brightly that we hear the remark that 'it is as bright as day'. This is far from being the case: about 500,000 full Moons would be needed to equal the light of the Sun. If you went to the Moon and looked back at the Earth you would see it larger and brighter than the Moon ever appears from Earth. It is because of this that we sometimes see the appearance of 'the old Moon in the new Moon's arms'. In addition to the thin bright sickle we see the dim outline of the rest of the Moon's near side. This shines with a greyish light and is due to *Earthshine*, or the light from the Earth reflected by the otherwise dark part of the Moon.

No doubt the Moon will one day affect the lives of everyone. The time will surely come when men will reach the Moon, land on its surface, and study its features at first-hand. Important steps have already been taken with this in mind, but the operation first man on the Moon will be one of stupendous difficulty. Several books have been published on the subject, and if you wish to keep up with developments you should subscribe to a good science magazine like *Discovery*, *The New Scientist* or *The Scientific American*. You could also join the British Interplanetary Society, which publishes a technical journal and *Spaceflight*, a magazine which deals with the more popular aspects of space research.

5

The Sun's Family

THE planets are bodies which, like the Earth, travel round
the Sun. They are of the Earth's order of size but vary a
great deal in size among themselves. Mercury, the smallest,
with a diameter of 3,100 miles, is only 1,000 miles larger
than the Moon. Jupiter, the largest, with a diameter of
88,700 miles at its equator, has a volume over 1,300 times
that of the Earth. But even Jupiter is quite small compared
with the Sun, which, as we have already seen, is well over a
million times larger than the Earth.

There are nine planets altogether, all at different distances
from the Sun. The Earth is the third one outwards. Between
us and the Sun lie the orbits of the so-called *inferior planets*
Mercury and Venus, and in this order outwards. Beyond us
lie the orbits of the *superior planets* Mars, Jupiter, Saturn,
Uranus, Neptune and Pluto. Pluto, the most distant one,
is nearly 40 times the Earth's distance from the Sun and
takes an average of about 248 years to complete one 'annual'
journey.

The entire system of Sun and planets is referred to as
the solar system. It is often represented in diagram form
in books and journals, but the diagrams, however excellent
in themselves, cannot begin to give a proper impression of
the immense distances involved. The same applies to
orreries, or mechanical models of the solar system sometimes found in museums. Many people, I find, carry around
with them the idea of a pocket-sized solar system; they have

retained a mental picture of the diagram but have over-
looked the importance of the distances involved. If you can,
obtain these distances and also the dimensions of the planets,
and then build up in imagination a scaled-down model.
Lay the whole thing out in a familiar field, with Pluto's
orbit just filling the field, or start off by making the Earth
the size of, say, a tennis ball. This approach was first suggested by Sir John Herschel, an astronomer who lived
about a century ago. Here are his own words:

'Choose any well-levelled field or bowling-green. On
it place a globe, 2 feet in diameter; this will represent the
Sun; Mercury will be represented by a grain of mustard
seed, on the circumference of a circle 164 feet in diameter
for its orbit; Venus a pea, on a circle of 284 feet in
diameter; the Earth also a pea, on a circle of 430 feet;
Mars a rather large pin's head, on a circle of 654 feet;
Jupiter a moderate-sized orange, on a circle nearly
half a mile across; Saturn a small orange, on a circle of
four-fifths of a mile; Uranus a full-sized cherry, or small
plum, upon the circumference of a circle more than a
mile and a half; and Neptune a good-sized plum, on a
circle about two miles and a half in diameter.'

Pluto was not discovered until 1930. In Herschel's model
it would be represented by another 'rather large pin's head'
(one of the old hatpin variety) on a circle about 3¼ miles in
diameter.

The planets, then, are quite tiny compared with the
enormous distances which separate them from one another.
The wonder is, in a way, that we can see them at all from
the Earth. By themselves they are all dark bodies, but
shine by reflecting the light of the Sun. Five of them—
Mercury, Venus, Mars, Jupiter and Saturn—are naked-eye
objects, with Uranus sometimes on the threshold of naked-
eye vision. Their brightness varies according to their dis-

tance from us. Venus is the brightest; it is not only a good reflector of sunlight but from time to time comes to within 25,000,000 miles from the Earth. This makes it our nearest neighbour among the planets. Mars, at a minimum distance of about 34,600,000 miles, is the next nearest, but he shines with a reddish light and is not a particularly good light reflector. Jupiter can outshine all the stars and planets with the exception of Venus at its brightest.

The planets all travel round the Sun in the same sense or direction, their speeds of travel decrease with increasing distance from the Sun, their orbits are ellipses, and the planes of those orbits lie fairly close to the plane of the ecliptic. These facts bear on the apparent movements of the planets as seen from the Earth, and we shall presently consider each one in turn.

But first, how to distinguish between a planet and a star. One guide is that stars twinkle, planets don't. Stars twinkle or *scintillate* when their light passes through moving layers of differently heated air. These air currents are very much about on clear frosty nights, as you will readily find if you study the stars in winter-time. Sirius sometimes twinkles so violently as to flash like a diamond, and with diamond colours too. Planets, however, are not points of light like the stars but subtend definite, although small, angles. They therefore shine with a much steadier light, although even they sometimes twinkle when fairly close to the horizon and when the air is greatly disturbed. Another guide is to look at the suspect through a pair of binoculars or small telescope. If it is a star it will still look like a point of light, but a planet can show a definite shape or size. Even this approach is not always reliable, for the telescope may not be powerful enough to resolve the planet into a planet. The best guide is to know your stars so that the planet stands out as an intruder. Even better, know your sky so well that you know approximately where each planet is at the time of observation.

Since the planets are all moving bodies, and since they are nearer to us than the stars, they appear to move against the starry background. Check this for yourself by plotting their positions on a star map night after night and week after week. You will find that they regularly trace out quite complicated paths among the stars. Their *general* movement, however, is from east to west, which shows that they all travel in the same sense or direction round the Sun. Mercury and Venus move much more quickly than the others and keep in the Sun's neighbourhood. Saturn moves slowest of all, spending on the average about two years in each constellation, while Jupiter spends about a year in each. This shows quite clearly that the further away a planet is from the Sun the longer it takes to travel once round the Sun. In addition, Mars, Jupiter and Saturn can often be seen in the southern part of the sky at midnight, but this never applies to Mercury and Venus. Mars, Jupiter and Saturn are therefore superior planets, while Mercury and Venus are inferior. Finally, they all move in the band or belt of the zodiac, in keeping with the fact that the solar system is a comparatively flat affair.

The apparent motion of a planet is a combination of its own motion and that of the Earth. Consider, for instance, the nature of the apparent motion of Venus. When the planet is in line with the Earth and the Sun, but on the far side of the Sun, it is said to be in *superior conjunction*. When it is again in line, but between the Sun and the Earth, it is in *inferior conjunction*. The time between two successive conjunctions of the same kind (superior or inferior) is called the *synodic period*. In the case of Venus it has an average value of 584 days. On its own, however, and unrelated to the Earth, Venus goes round the Sun in a period of about 225 days. Its *sidereal period*, or period relative to the stars, is therefore 225 days. For Mercury the synodic period averages nearly 116 days, but the average sidereal period is only about 88 days.

In the case of a superior planet like Mars, the planet is in conjunction when it is in line with the Sun and Earth and on the far side of the Sun. It is in *opposition* when it is again in line but on our side of the Sun. Its average synodic period, or the time between two successive conjunctions or oppositions, is 780 days, while the sidereal period is 687 days. Jupiter and Saturn have average synodic periods of

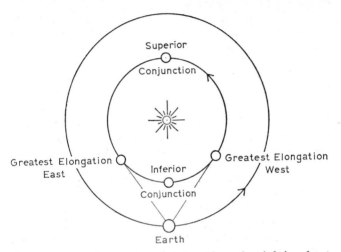

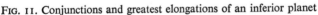

FIG. 11. Conjunctions and greatest elongations of an inferior planet

399 days and 378 days respectively, and sidereal periods of nearly 12 years and $29\frac{1}{2}$ years respectively.

If you plot the changes in position of a planet among the stars over a long enough interval of time you will find that it traces out a zigzag curve. This is due in part to the fact that the planet's apparent motion is a combination of its own orbital motion and that of the Earth. From time to time the two planets are so placed in their orbits that there is no relative motion; the other planet therefore appears to stand still or be *stationary*. The general pattern of behaviour is this: the planet proceeds in a direct or east-to-west direction, slows down, becomes stationary, speeds up and proceeds in a retrograde or west-to-east direction, slows down, becomes stationary, speeds up and proceeds with direct motion. The zigzag curve is also due in part to the fact that the planet moves in an orbit slightly inclined to the ecliptic. The curve sometimes contains one or two loops, called *loops of retrogression*.

The loops are nicely shown in the planetarium when the events of a year are compressed into 10 seconds. The planetarium Sun is made to circuit the artificial sky once in 10 seconds. The Moon and planet projectors are all geared to the Sun projector, and in such a way that the planetarium Moon and planets all go through their correct proportionate movements. The effect is particularly striking with the planet Mars which in a matter of minutes is seen to make successive loops in Gemini (1961), Cancer (1963), Leo (1965), and Virgo (1967). Mercury and Venus dash round with the Sun. Jupiter and Saturn just swing slowly from side to side in a leisurely and sedate fashion, but always with an underlying direct motion.

We can now consider each of the planets in turn, mainly with a view to becoming fairly expert not only in knowing where to find them but also in accounting for their changes in brightness and position.

Mercury. Since Mercury is the nearest planet to the Sun it is seen in the Sun's neighbourhood. As it travels round the Sun it appears to swing from east to west of the Sun. It can therefore be seen just after sunset as an evening star, or just before sunrise as a morning star. Its greatest angular distance, or maximum *elongation* east or west of the Sun, varies from 18° to 28°. This keeps it in the Sun's twilight glow before sunrise or after sunset, makes it appear less bright than it really is and makes it difficult to find. In itself it is a bright object, and at its best can equal Sirius in brilliancy and be exceeded only by Venus, Mars and Jupiter.

The best time to see Mercury would appear to be when
its elongation is at the maximum of 28° at a time when the
ecliptic at sunrise or sunset is most steeply inclined to the
horizon. This suggests a maximum eastern elongation
occurring in spring and a maximum western elongation
occurring in autumn. Unfortunately, the extreme limits of

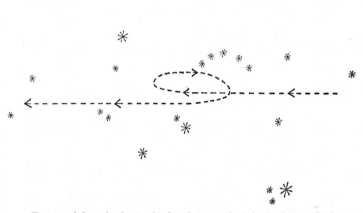

FIG. 12. A loop in the track of a planet against the background of
stars

28° are reached when the planet has a negative Decl., or
when it lies southwards of the Sun. It is therefore more
favourably placed at elongations of only 18° or 20° when
it has a positive Decl., or when it lies northwards of the
Sun. Under these circumstances it can remain above the
horizon for about two hours after sunset.

The telescope shows that Mercury goes through a complete cycle of phases in a synodic period of about 116 days.
This is because it moves in an orbit inside the Earth's and
so shows us different parts of its sunlit side at different times.

E

But unlike the phases of the Moon, those of Mercury are associated with a change in apparent size (owing to the change in distance), with consequent change in brightness. About the time of elongation Mercury looks like a half-Moon: it is a full disk at superior conjunction. The actual phase depends, of course, on the positions of Mercury and the Sun with respect to the Earth.

Mercury is difficult to observe with a telescope. Besides being small (about 6 to 9 seconds of arc in apparent diameter), it has to be studied through a considerable thickness of air which upsets the definition. Astronomers therefore usually study it during the afternoon or morning when it is higher up. Knowing its position in R.A. and Decl. they can set their telescopes accordingly and so pick it up and follow it during broad daylight.

When Mercury is at inferior conjunction it is sometimes also on or very near the ecliptic. It then appears as a black circular spot on the bright face of the Sun. Its passage across the Sun's disk is called a *transit*. These are fairly frequent events, but owing to Mercury's small size, they cannot be seen without a telescope. They occur either in May or November. The last was on November 7th, 1960. The next will be on May 9th, 1970, to be followed by another on November 9th, 1973.

Venus. Like Mercury, Venus appears to swing from east to west of the Sun. Its elongation can be as much as 47°. In addition, it is larger than Mercury (the diameter is 7,700 miles), is an extremely good reflector of sunlight and at times comes to within 25,000,000 miles of the Earth. This makes it a brilliant object, especially when it reaches its eastern and western elongations. Yet the times of greatest brilliancy occur some weeks after eastern elongation and some weeks before western elongation. This is because the brightness depends not on the elongation but on the phase and associated apparent diameter. In other words, it depends on the apparent area of what we can see of the planet's sunlit side. On these occasions the phase is a crescent and the diameter about 40 seconds of arc. The diameter varies from $9''\cdot5$ at superior to $65''$ at inferior conjunction, and averages $25''$ at elongations. One complete phase cycle occurs in the synodic period of 584 days.

When Venus shines brightly in the morning or evening sky around Christmas there are always those who associate it with the 'Star of Bethlehem'—and to the point of thinking

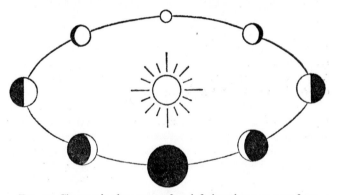

FIG. 13. Changes in the aspect of an inferior planet as seen from the Earth

that the 'Star' has returned. This happened as recently as Christmas, 1960. Venus just forces itself on the attention, even being visible in daylight and causing objects to cast perceptible shadows at night. It has, of course, nothing whatever to do with the 'Star of Bethlehem', which, if it was a natural event, was something quite different. Venus, along with the other naked-eye planets, was observed and studied long before the Christian era. Its very brilliance, however, makes it a difficult object for study through a telescope. Astronomers therefore observe it in daytime, when it is both less brilliant and higher up in the sky.

Transits of Venus are much rarer than those of Mercury.

The last occurred in 1882, but the next will not take place until 2004.

Mars (Plate 7). Unlike Mercury and Venus, Mars can wander right away from the Sun to appear on the celestial meridian at midnight. It is then at opposition, or in a direction opposite to that of the Sun, and shines with a brilliant reddish light. This colour comes from its surface, for Mars has a thin atmosphere comparatively free from clouds.

Some oppositions are more favourable than others in the sense that Mars is closer to us at some oppositions than at others. Oppositions occur at intervals of 780 days, or just over 2 years 2 months. But since Mars moves in a fairly elliptical orbit, its distance at opposition can vary from 34,600,000 miles to 62,900,000 miles. The most favourable oppositions occur in August and September and are repeated at intervals of 15 to 17 years. Mars then has an apparent diameter of 30 seconds of arc. They occurred in August, 1939 and 1956: the next will therefore take place in August, 1971. The least favourable oppositions occur in February or March, and are repeated at the same intervals. One occurred in March, 1950. The next will take place in February, 1963, and March, 1965.

Mars is best placed for observation in northerly latitudes when it has maximum northern Decl. at the time of favourable opposition. The inclination of its orbit to the ecliptic is 1° 51'. Hence on occasions Mars can be as high as nearly 64° above the London skyline at midnight or as low as about 13°. Around the time of opposition the Earth closes in and draws apart from Mars quite rapidly, which makes the time a good one for plotting the planet's apparent path against the starry background.

Jupiter (Plate 7). Jupiter, the brightest of all the planets with the exception of Venus, is sometimes bright enough to be seen in daytime. Its synodic period is 399 days, so it is therefore in opposition at intervals of about 13 months. About that time it goes through only a small change in

THE SUN'S FAMILY 69

apparent size, and at favourable oppositions can be as
large as 50 seconds of arc. It also remains on view for a
large part of the year, being beyond reach only near the
times of conjunction with the Sun.

Jupiter is especially prominent for northern observers
when its Decl. is about $+24°$ at opposition. Its altitude at
midnight can then be 62° above the London skyline. This
happens at intervals of 12 years; the same holds for southern
observers when the Decl. is about $-24°$.

A good pair of binoculars or small telescope will make it
clear that Jupiter is no star. The planet shows a definite disk
and is accompanied by four moons or satellites. It has
twelve satellites altogether, but the others are all faint
objects. These four were discovered in 1610 by Galileo when
he turned one of the first telescopes towards Jupiter. They
looked like stars, but by watching them night after night,
Galileo saw that they appeared to swing from side to side of
the planet itself.

Don't be surprised if you fail to see all four satellites: one
or more may be passing behind or crossing in front of
Jupiter. On occasions all four disappear. Each one is then
either in transit across Jupiter's face, eclipsed by its shadow,
or *occulted*, that is, hidden behind its disk. These transits,
eclipses and occultations are a constant source of interest and
can be seen quite easily with a good 3-inch refracting telescope. If you have a small telescope, therefore, keep a regular
check on the positions of the satellites and try to identify
them. Their names, periods, distances etc., are as follows:

	Approx. distance from Jupiter (miles)		Approx. Sidereal period (days)	Diameter (miles)	Stellar mag.
I.	Io	264,000	1·8	2,000	5½
II.	Europa	420,000	3·6	1,750	6
III.	Ganymede	670,000	7·2	3,000	5
IV.	Callisto	1,177,000	16·7	2,800	6

As a further guide, refer to the tables in the B.A.A. *Handbook*. These give the configurations of the four satellites as seen in an inverting telescope in the northern hemisphere. They also give information about satellite transits, eclipses and occultations. By referring to these tables, therefore, you will have no difficulty in identifying the satellites at any particular time.

The last column in our table shows that the satellites are about equal in brightness to the faintest stars visible on a clear night. Several people claim to have seen the satellites with the unaided eye, and without knowing their configurations beforehand. The fact is that the satellites lie so close to Jupiter's brilliant body that most people need a telescope if they are to see them at all.

Jupiter is slightly oval in shape, being 88,700 miles across at the equator and 82,000 miles between the poles. This polar flattening can be seen in small telescopes, also the dark and light bands or belts which stretch across the disk parallel to one another and to the planet's equator. These bands are belts of clouds which completely hide the surface (if there is one) from view.

Saturn (Plate 7). Saturn shines with a rather dull, yellowish light but is brighter than ordinary first-magnitude stars. Its synodic period is 378 days, or 13 days longer than a year, so it comes into opposition 13 days later every year. During opposition its apparent diameter is about 20 seconds of arc. Like Mars and Jupiter, Saturn is prominent for northern observers when it reaches a high northern Decl. about the time of opposition. At present (1962) Saturn is in the southerly part of the zodiac and will not cross the equator again until 1966.

Saturn is the only planet to have a system of rings. Small telescopes don't show them as rings, but they can be seen as such with refractors of 3 inches aperture and above. Their aspect changes, however, so that they are sometimes seen well open, and sometimes not at all. They disappear completely at intervals of 15 years when they are turned edgeways to the Earth. This shows that they are quite narrow (about 20 miles) in relation to their width (about 40,000 miles).

Saturn has nine moons, but only one, Titan, and possibly another, Rhea, can be seen with a small telescope. They look like faint stars of magnitude 8 and 10 respectively. Their positions throughout the greater part of the year are given in the B.A.A. *Handbook*.

Uranus. At an average distance from the Sun of 1,782,000,000 miles, Uranus at opposition is no brighter than a star of about the 6th magnitude. It can therefore be seen with the unaided eye—provided you know where to look. Its path among the stars is shown in the B.A.A. *Handbook*, and from this you could easily pick it up with binoculars. At opposition its apparent diameter is only about 4 seconds of arc, which means that it will still look starlike in small telescopes. It takes about 84 years to travel once round the Sun, and therefore spends about 4 years in each constellation of the zodiac. It moved into Leo from Cancer in 1960, and passed slightly south of *Regulus* at the end of 1961. It will cross the celestial equator going south in about 1980.

Its mean or average distance from the Sun, 1,782,000,000 miles, is easily remembered, for it was discovered in 1781. It had been seen several times before but had been mistaken for a star. On the night of March 13th, 1781, Sir William Herschel picked it up in his 6·3-inch aperture reflector, and straightway recognized it as something unusual. It showed a perceptible disk, and on following nights moved slowly among the stars. Herschel thought that he had discovered a comet but it was later shown to be a planet and given the name Uranus.

Neptune and Pluto (Plate 7). These two extremely distant planets are both objects for the telescope. Neptune at its brightest is about magnitude 8, and Pluto about magnitude

14. The path of Neptune is given in the B.A.A. *Handbook*, which also gives the R.A. and Decl. of Pluto for 10-day intervals. Neptune crossed the celestial equator going south in 1944 and will remain south of the equator until about 2028.

The Astronomical Ephemeris or B.A.A. *Handbook*, used in conjunction with *Norton's Star Atlas*, provide all that is necessary for finding the planets. Simpler information, in descriptive form, will be found in *Whitaker's Almanack* and in the astronomical columns of *The Times* and *The Daily Telegraph* newspapers. These columns appear on the first weekday of the month and include a small monthly star chart. *The Times* also publishes these charts in booklet form as a series of twelve before the beginning of each year. A monthly sky diary appears in *Hermes*, the journal of the J.A.S., and another is given each month in *Sky and Telescope*.

The Astronomical Ephemeris also contains tables of the predicted positions in R.A. and Decl. of four minor planets: Ceres, Pallas, Juno and Vesta. Similar information is given in the B.A.A. *Handbook*, but for 10-day intervals, and sometimes the positions of one or more other minor planets which may be within the reach of small telescopes.

What are minor planets, and how easy or difficult are they to find? They are small bodies which move in the main between the orbits of Mars and Jupiter with periods of 4 or 5 years. There are probably over 100,000 of them, but so far only about 1,600 have been observed thoroughly enough to have their orbits determined. Ceres, the largest, was discovered in 1801. It is only about 450 miles in diameter, and at an average distance of 260,000,000 miles from the Sun has a sidereal period of 4 years 7 months. At opposition its distance from the Earth is therefore about 167,000,000 miles. Small wonder, then, that its magnitude is about $7\frac{1}{2}$. If you wish to observe it you will need a small telescope or pair of binoculars, also a star atlas which goes down to stars fainter than those in Norton. Pallas, diameter

275 miles, has an average opposition magnitude of 8·0. Juno, diameter 150 miles, has magnitude 8·7, while Vesta, diameter 250 miles, is the brightest with magnitude 6·5.

A suitable star atlas for use in finding and following the four minor planets mentioned above is *Atlas Eclipticalis 1950·0*. This consists of a bound set of 32 star charts prepared by Antonin Becvar and his colleagues at the Skalnate Pleso Observatory, Czechoslovakia. It covers declinations between +30° and −30° and shows stars down to magnitude 9·0. Becvar has also produced an *Atlas Coeli 1950·0*, or atlas of the heavens for epoch 1950·0, which covers the entire sky down to stellar magnitude 7·75. The various editions of these charts are advertised regularly in *Sky and Telescope* and can be obtained through Sky Publishing Corporation, Harvard Observatory, Cambridge 38, Mass., U.S.A.

Quite often two or more major planets come into close *conjunction*, or appear fairly close together. Sometimes the Moon joins in as well, to provide a display which impresses even the most casual watcher of the skies. The Moon can also temporarily hide or occult a bright star or planet, while on rare occasions a planet can occult a star.

Occultations of stars are listed every year in the B.A.A. *Handbook* and *The Astronomical Ephemeris*. If you have a small telescope and know in advance when a bright star will be occulted, notice how suddenly the star disappears when it reaches the Moon's limb, also how suddenly it reappears. This shows that the Moon has no appreciable atmosphere. If it had the star would gradually fade on one side of the Moon and gradually brighten on the other. This effect was actually observed on July 7th, 1959, when Venus occulted *Regulus*, although it was known beforehand that Venus has an atmosphere. Venus had never before been observed to occult a bright star, although in 1737 Dr. Bevis saw an occultation of Mercury by Venus. Calculations show that on the average Venus occults *Regulus* once every

530 years and that the next occultation will not take place until October 1st, 2044.

Sometimes the Sun, Moon and five naked-eye planets all meet in one fairly small part of the sky. This happened in early February, 1962. Not so long ago people believed that close groupings of this kind spelled great disaster, even the end of the world. The great bubonic plague called the Black Death was thought by some to be caused by a grouping of Mars, Jupiter and Saturn in Aquarius, The Water Carrier. These planets met again in Pisces, The Fishes, on February 20th, 1524, which led astrologers (and some astronomers too) to predict a universal flood. As a result, many people left their homes for the hills or built boats large enough to hold their families and worldly possessions.

Just before Christmas, 1603, the astronomer Johannes Kepler observed a close conjunction of Jupiter and Saturn in Pisces. He remembered that a Jewish writer had previously referred to an old Jewish belief that the Messiah would appear when Jupiter and Saturn met in Pisces. He therefore calculated previous conjunctions of this type and found that there had been a threefold one in the year now reckoned as 7 B.C. Was this the sign in the sky that led the Wise Men to undertake their long journey to Jerusalem? Some scholars think that it was. They find that the first encounter of Jupiter and Saturn in Pisces occurred in May of that year; the two planets then appeared in the east before sunrise. They met again in October, and for a third time in December, but each time in Pisces. Now the Wise Men were probably astrologers; they would have regarded Jupiter as a royal star, Saturn as the protective star of Israel, and Pisces as the sign of Messiah. At no time did they mistake the 'stars' for one, but with their astrological background, so scholars suggest, the event would have been regarded as one of the utmost significance.

We now know that single conjunctions of Jupiter and Saturn occur at intervals of approximately 20 years. Three-

fold conjunctions occur on the average once every 120
years. The last one was in 1940–1, and the next will take
place in 1981.

No account of the solar system would be complete without
mention of comets and meteorites, for these are just as much
members of the Sun's family as are the major and minor
planets (Plate 15). Quite a large number of comets are discovered every century, but most of them are extremely
faint objects far below the limits of the unaided eye. Comets
usually arouse public interest when they are large and
bright enough to attract attention and receive mention in
the newspapers. But objects of this type are usually few
and far between, especially so far during the present century.
You probably saw the two in 1957 (Comet Arend-Roland
in April, and Comet Mrkos in August) and may be old
enough to recall seeing the 1910 appearance of Halley's
Comet. I have met quite a lot of people who saw Halley's
Comet. Their memory wasn't very good when it came to
recalling other things, but they remembered the comet.

If you are fortunate enough to see a comet don't give it
just a casual glance and then vanish indoors. Notice just
where it is in relation to the stars and try to plot its path
by making nightly observations. At the same time try to
judge the brightness of its *nucleus*, or star-like brightest
part, and see for how far you can trace its tail. Usually the
longer you stay in the dark, so allowing the eyes to get
really dark-adapted, the further you should be able to trace
the tail. Notice, incidentally, that quite faint stars can be
seen through the tail: it must therefore be thinner than the
finest cloud. A series of observations like these should show
that the comet's tail points away from the Sun, and that it
usually grows in size and brightness as the comet gets closer
to the Sun. If it is on its way to the Sun you may even have
a chance of seeing it on its return journey.

Comets usually move in very elongated orbits and in this
respect differ completely from the planets. A comet is at

perihelion when it is closest to the Sun. Some get danger-
ously close. The great comet of 1882, for example, almost
grazed the Sun, being only about 290,000 miles away
from the Sun's surface at perihelion. Its period was 760
years and its greatest distance, or distance at *aphelion*, was
16,000,000,000 miles. It therefore spends the greater part
of its period beyond the orbit of Pluto. Yet compared with
the periods of some comets, that of the comet of 1882 is
quite short. Quite a number have periods which run into
thousands of years.

The most famous comet of all is Halley's Comet. This
has an average period of 77 years, but the interval has been
as short as 74·5 years and as long as 79·3 years. These
variations are due to perturbations—to the disturbing
influence of the giant planets Jupiter, Saturn, Uranus and
Neptune. Its last perihelion passage was in 1910. At present
it is moving beyond the orbit of Neptune, but by 1980 it
should be within the orbit of Uranus, and 1986 should see
the next perihelion passage. Records kept by the ancient
Chinese enable us to trace its appearances right back to
240 B.C., so it has been in existence for at least 2,000 years
and probably much longer.

The apparent length of a comet's tail depends on its
actual length, its distance, and the angle at which we see it.
Comet 1861 II (i.e. the second comet to pass perihelion
in 1861) at one stage had a tail 118° long, which corres-
ponded to an actual distance of over 42,000,000 miles.
But quite a number of comets have had tails longer than
this. The record for length goes to Comet 1841. It grew a
tail which stretched 198,000,000 miles into space, or over
twice the distance of the Earth from the Sun. On May 20th,
1910, the tail of Halley's Comet stretched out 150°, or nearly
across the entire sky. The *head*, or brightest part of the
comet, was then only about 14,000,000 miles away, and on
the following day the Earth actually passed through the
tail, but without any untoward effects.

The total quantity of matter in a comet runs into millions of millions of tons. Even so, it is still almost negligible in mass compared with the Earth. If a comet happened to come close to the Earth it would not perturb the Earth, or deflect it from its course. Rather would it be appreciably perturbed by the Earth. In 1770, for example, Lexell's Comet came within 1,500,000 miles of the Earth, but without causing a change of any kind. The Earth perturbed the comet, however, and to the extent of changing the period by several days. Most of the material in a comet lies not in

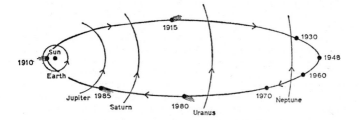

FIG. 14. The path of Halley's Comet

the tail but in the head, and then in the brightest part, or nucleus. The nucleus itself probably consists of a spongy mass of frozen gases and stony lumps of iron. Yet even if the nucleus hit the Earth head on we should experience nothing more serious than a number of explosive impacts and a spectacular shower of shooting stars.

Shooting stars or *meteors* can be seen on any clear night, provided there is not too much moonlight to lighten the sky. If you would like to see them in fairly large numbers, pick on one of the more favourable annual showers. Every year there are a number of showers of shooting stars which occur on time with great regularity. They are listed in the B.A.A. *Handbook* along with notes as to the expected maximum hourly number and general observing conditions.

The meteors in any one of these showers are quite small bodies. Those which we see are usually about the size of a grain of sand but appear larger owing to their swift flight through the Earth's atmosphere. They come from inter-planetary space, dash into the thin upper air at speeds of many miles a second and by rubbing against the air become white hot. The air in contact with them also gets so hot as to shine, and this along with the hot vaporized parts of the meteor itself accounts for its brilliance and for the faint streak or train which it sometimes leaves behind. The train may last for a few minutes, but usually disappears in a few seconds. In any case, meteors of this size are completely vaporized long before they reach the ground.

The meteors in each annual shower appear to streak away from a particular constellation. If their paths are traced backwards in the sky they will be found to converge to a small area or, in some cases, to almost a point. This point is called the *radiant*. It is really an effect of perspective and is analogous to a distant view of some railway lines. Although the lines are parallel to each other they appear to converge to a point or small region in the distance. The meteors too travel in parallel paths both inside and outside the Earth's atmosphere.

To understand how meteors behave in space consider the case of the Perseid shower. These are meteors which appear to come from a radiant in Perseus. They spread their visit over the last days of July and the first two weeks of August and reach a maximum of about 50 an hour around August 12th. They appear year after year, but always in late July and early August, and there are records of them appearing at this time for over 1,200 years. This regularity is due to the fact that they belong to a stream of meteoric particles distributed in a diffuse ring around the Sun. Every August the Earth passes through the stream, gathering up particles as would a vacuum cleaner passing through a swarm of gnats.

Almost a century ago the Italian astronomer Schiaparelli found that the Perseid meteors moved in an orbit almost identical with that of a fairly faint comet which appeared in 1862. This strongly suggested that the comet and the meteors were closely connected, or better, that they had a common origin. A few years later, Schiaparelli, Leverrier and others identified the orbit of the November Leonids with Tempel's Comet of 1866. This second identification sparked off a real hunt for other pairs of comets and meteor showers moving in identical orbits. As a result several more pairs were found, and we now have good reasons for thinking that every major meteor shower is associated with a comet.

The comet associated with the Perseids is Comet Swift-Tuttle. It has a period of nearly 120 years so we don't expect to see it again until 1982. Its orbit, and therefore that of the Perseid meteors, is tilted almost at right angles to the plane of the Earth's orbit. This modifies the usual picture of the solar system as a rather flat affair, with the planets and comets all moving fairly close to the plane of the Earth's orbit. Here are bodies (and they are by no means the only ones) which keep aloof from the general trend. This gives them one great advantage: at no time do they pass near a large planet like Jupiter or Saturn to be perturbed.

Another major annual shower is that of the Geminids. They appear in mid-December, to reach a maximum rate of about 60 meteors an hour on December 12th and December 13th. They are one of the few showers which have no known associated comet. Their own elliptical orbit, however, has been well established, and they are known to travel round the Sun once in about 1·6 years.

In the last century the most striking displays were given by the November Leonids. They are associated with Comet 1866 I, or Tempel's Comet. They seem to have attracted little general attention until November 12th, 1833, when they gave a wonderful display over America. One eye-witness described them as being as 'thick as snow coming down in a snowstorm'. A similar display occurred in 1866, which led astronomers to predict another for 1899. But on this last occasion Jupiter perturbed the stream to such an extent that it gave only a poor display. Since then the Leonids have been comparatively few in number and are now of little interest. Even Tempel's Comet, due to return in 1932, failed to appear.

So far during this century the best displays have been those of the Draconids in October, 1933 and 1946. Because of their association with Comet Giacobini-Zinner they are sometimes referred to as the Giacobinids. They were also studied by radar techniques in 1946 and again on October 9th, 1952.

The various members of the Sun's far-flung family therefore provide plenty to read about and watch. A telescope is not essential when you begin, but it can be a great help and stimulus to further studies. If you have one and would like to pursue the matter further, then join the J.A.S. or B.A.A. The latter has separate sections for the observation of Mercury and Venus, Mars, Jupiter and Saturn, also for meteors and comets. In addition, the Association publishes a *Circular* which gives up-to-date information about major changes in planetary features and the appearances and positions of any newly discovered comets.

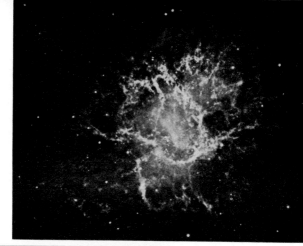

Plate 8.
The Crab Nebula.
Photographed
with the 200-inch
telescope of the
Mount Wilson
and Palomar
Observatories

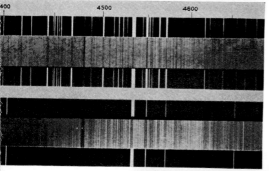

Plate 9.
Spectrograms of
the Spectroscopic
Binary Mizar,
showing the lines
doubled (Yerkes
Observatory)

Plate 10.
The Pleiades
(Lick Observatory)

Plate 11.'
The Great Nebula
in Orion (Lick
Observatory)

Plate 12.
Part of the Milky
Way (Harvard
College
Observatory)

6

The Stars as Suns

I ALWAYS envy those who, anxious to know something about the stars, read their first book on astronomy. Theirs is essentially a fresh approach to an old subject, whereas mine is invariably tempered by the thought that I have 'read all about it before'. Not that the sky itself loses its charm and interest with the passing years, for it is ever changing and has a never-ending fascination. I shall always remember my first book on astronomy. It was Sir Robert Ball's *The Story of the Heavens*. I have it still, its pages and covers worn through frequent use. It was a good friend and guide for several years, for I could afford no other, but then came Hutchinson's *Splendour of the Heavens*. This was a magnificent book, large in size, profusely illustrated and packed full of information about almost every aspect of astronomy. Copies are now few and far between, for the book went out of print many years ago. It was, in my opinion, the most wonderful book of all.

I am convinced that it is no use reading books like these or their modern counterparts unless, wherever possible, their information is referred to the actual sky itself. It's a case of reading two books at once, one written in words and bound between two covers, the other written in stars and spread across the sky. Our aim must therefore be to encourage this dual reading so that a study of the stars becomes both an indoor and an outdoor activity.

Sooner or later in your reading you will come up against the term *light-year*. It's a problem word at the Planetarium, for most people have never heard of it before, and you cannot conveniently talk about the distances of the stars without using it. Yet many people react by remarking that they cannot 'begin to understand a light-year', while others say: 'I followed you until you mentioned light-years but then had to give up.'

One feels that in many cases it is not a case of not understanding the meaning of the term but rather one of an unwillingness to make the mental effort to bring about an understanding. After all, the mental jump from a mile to a light-year is no different in kind than that involved in moving from the concept of a millimetre to a mile. In brief, a light-year is the distance light travels in a year. In a second it travels 186,283 miles, or in round figures 186,000 miles. In a year, therefore, it travels just under 6,000,000,000,000 miles, or about 63,000 times the distance of the Earth from the Sun.

So distant are the stars that their distances stated in miles would be as meaningless as the distance from London to New York expressed in millimetres. A star like *Altair*, for example, is 12 light-years away. We therefore see it not as it is, but as it was 12 years ago. The Sun, on the other hand, is about $8\frac{1}{3}$ light-minutes away, so a comparison between the distance of Altair and that of the Sun is one of 12 years with $8\frac{1}{3}$ minutes. There is no intrinsic difficulty in understanding this, although it should be born in mind that there are nearly 526,000 minutes in a year. The best plan is to remember that *Proxima Centauri*, the Sun's next-door neighbour among the stars, is $4\frac{1}{3}$ light-years away. This can then be taken as a standard of reference when dealing with the distances of other stars. Of course, $4\frac{1}{3}$ light-years by Earthly standards is a fantastically great distance. When Major Gagarin made his historic flight round the Earth he travelled at a speed of about 18,000 miles an hour. Yet a journey to *Proxima Centauri* at this speed would take him about 140,000 years, or 2,000 lifetimes each of 70 years.

Proxima Centauri is a star of the 11th magnitude in the southern hemisphere. It lies near *Alpha Centauri* with which it is associated through the invisible bonds of gravitation. *Alpha Centauri* itself is not one star but two, with nearby *Proxima* making a third. The system is therefore one of three suns. The nearest star in the northern hemisphere is *61 Cygni*, a double star, or system of two suns which circle round each other once in 720 years. Each star is approximately of the 6th magnitude, and together they appear as one star of about the 4th magnitude. *61 Cygni* is shown in *Norton's Star Atlas:* it forms an almost equal-sided triangle with *Deneb*, or *Alpha Cygni*, and *Gamma Cygni*. Its distance is 11·2 light-years. Bright *Sirius*, at a distance of 8·7 light-years, is another near neighbour but, since it lies south of the celestial equator, it is essentially a star in the southern hemisphere.

When dealing with the distances of the nearest stars make your own mental model as Sir John Herschel did when he sketched his model solar system. Let an inch, say, represent a light-year. Then *Proxima Centauri* would be $4\frac{1}{3}$ inches away, *Altair* 12 inches, *Betelgeuse* 54 feet, *Deneb* 133 feet and so on. As you learn the names of the brightest stars and locate them in the sky, learn also their distances, trying all the time to achieve a three-dimensional picture. After all, the stars are suns distributed in depth in space, and while two stars may appear close together in the sky it does not follow necessarily that they *are* close together in space. Only too often I meet people who have read books on astronomy but who still have no clear mental picture of the immensity of interstellar distances. They form a kind of pocket-book image of the universe which is quite innocent of proportion and scale. They are usually surprised to hear that if they could reach the Moon in $2\frac{1}{2}$ hours, a journey to the Sun would take 5 weeks, but one to *Proxima Centauri* would take about 30,000 years! But these are things which one can easily work out by long multiplication.

These distances, like all other measurements in science, are estimates only. When you measure, say, the length of a piece of wood, you compare it with another piece of wood divided into inches and fractions of an inch. You are probably satisfied with a result to the nearest sixteenth of an inch. But is this the length of the piece of wood? If you measured it with an accurately made micrometer you might find that the length is not 6·125 inches, say, but 6·1254 inches. If you measured it with a special optical device called an interferometer you might find that it is not 6·1254 inches but 6·12547 inches.

In rather the same way astronomers obtain slightly different results when they measure the distances of the stars in different ways. They prefer, then, to talk about estimated distances rather than the actual distances. What, for example, is the actual distance of the Sun? Nobody knows. Different methods give slightly different results, but it appears to be no less than 92,911,000 miles. It may be some 23,000 miles more than this. This is, of course, the average or mean distance of the Earth from the Sun. Astronomers call it *one astronomical unit* (1.A.U.), and use it when they estimate the distances of the nearest stars.

The stars are so distant that despite their great size they look like points of light even through a large telescope. When you magnify them more and more, however, they each begin to show a definite disk. This appearance is a spurious disk or *Airy disk* caused by the wave nature of light and the fact that the object-glass of a telescope is round. If it were square instead of round the spurious disk would appear square shaped. The disk has no bearing whatever upon the star itself. The same applies to photographs of the stars. The brighter stars look larger than the fainter ones, but this is purely a photographic effect which increases with increasing time of exposure.

The fact that the stars are all at different distances from us does not on its own account for their differences in brightness. They differ among themselves in actual or intrinsic brightness or, as we say in astronomy, *luminosity*. There are stars many thousands of times more luminous than the Sun, and stars only a tiny fraction as luminous. These differences in luminosity arise from differences in size and temperature. A large star has a greater surface area than a small star. If both stars have the same temperature the larger will therefore be the more luminous of the two. Large size accompanied by high surface temperature (about 20,000°C.) produces a star of high luminosity. The Sun, a little below average in both size and temperature, is therefore slightly below average in luminosity also.

An easy way of comparing the luminosities of the stars is to imagine that they are all at the same distance from us. This standard distance is taken as $32\frac{1}{2}$ light-years, or 10 parsecs (1 parsec $= 3.259$ light-years). The magnitude of a star calculated for this distance is called the *absolute magnitude*. When this is done it is found that the absolute magnitudes of the great majority of stars are included within the range -5 to $+15$, with the Sun's absolute magnitude of 4.86 occupying a nearly central position.

The discussion of these and other characteristics of the stars is the province of *astrophysics*. This is a most fascinating subject, but to understand it at even an elementary level requires a sound knowledge of mathematics and physics. Several books cover the ground quite well, introducing the reader to terms such as spectrum, emission lines, Doppler shift, trigonometrical parallax. Previous knowledge of mathematics and physics is not essential for an understanding of the principles of astrophysics but it certainly helps.

In order to ferret out the physical characteristics of the

stars astronomers usually require a knowledge of three
things: (1) *Brightness or apparent magnitude.* This can be
measured with great accuracy by photoelectric techniques.
(2) *Distance.* This is estimated for a fairly near star by
measuring its parallax by a trigonometrical method. This
is explained in every elementary textbook on astronomy.
The method gets less reliable over increasing distances.
For very distant stars one or more other methods are used.
(3) *Spectral class.* This is obtained by studying and measuring
a *spectrogram*, or photograph of the spectrum of a star. A
knowledge of (1) and (2) gives the absolute magnitude and
luminosity. A knowledge of (3) gives the temperature.
Knowing the temperature and the spectral class, astronomers
can calculate the size. The following table gives the apparent
magnitudes, absolute magnitudes, luminosities and distances of some of the brightest stars. Notice how great
distance causes even a highly luminous star to appear
comparatively faint.

Name	Apparent mag.	Absolute mag.	Luminosity (Sun=1)	Distance (light-years)
Sun	−26·72	+4·86	1·0	
Sirius	−1·47	+1·36	26	8·7
Canopus	−0·71	−7·4	80,000	300
Arcturus	0·06	−0·2	100	36
Vega	0·03	+0·6	50	26
Rigel	0·08	−5·8	18,000	850
Procyon	0·34	+2·8	5·4	11
Altair	0·75	+2·4	9	12
Aldebaran	0·78	−0·1	90	65
Antares	0·92	−4·0	3,400	400
Betelgeuse	0·92	−2·9	1,200	650

The next table shows how the comparatively small range
in surface temperature and diameter combine to give a
much greater range of luminosity.

Name	Surface Temp. (°K)*	Diameter (Sun=1)	Luminosity (Sun=1)
Sun	6,000	1·0	1·0
Sirius	11,200	1·8	26
Canopus	8,000	210	80,000
Arcturus	4,100	23	100
Vega	11,200	2·4	50
Rigel	12,500	42	18,000
Procyon	6,500	1·7	5·4
Altair	8,600	1·3	9
Aldebaran	3,300	36	90
Antares	3,400	285	3,400
Betelgeuse	3,100	300-420	1,200

*°K refers to degrees Kelvin. They are degrees Centigrade reckoned on a scale which begins at −273°C. or absolute zero. To convert °K into °C subtract 273.

When all the stars are studied in this way we find that most of them can be arranged in a sequence of decreasing temperature, size and luminosity. This sequence is called the *main sequence*. At the top are high-temperature stars about 10 times the diameter of the Sun. *Beta Centauri* is a typical top-of-the-sequence star. Of apparent magnitude 0·6 it looks almost as bright as *Alpha Centauri*. Yet its distance is 300 light-years. With a diameter 11 times the Sun's and a surface temperature of 21,000°K., it is over 3,000 times more luminous than the Sun. The high surface temperature means that it shines with an intense bluish-white light. The Sun, also in the main sequence, has a surface temperature of 6,000°K. At this temperature, well below the average, the Sun is a yellowish star. Near the bottom of the sequence are stars like *Barnard's Star*, *61 Cygni A* (the more luminous of the two components of *61 Cygni*), and *Krüger 60*. These are orange in colour and both smaller and cooler than the Sun.

Another group of stars are the far less common *giant stars*. These are large and luminous, but they have comparatively low surface temperatures. *Arcturus* is a member of the group. As Tables I and II showed, *Arcturus* is 1000 times as luminous as the Sun and 23 times the size of the Sun. With a surface temperature of 4,100°K. it is cooler than the Sun and therefore shines with an orange light. *Aldebaran* is another giant star. Its orange colour is quite noticeable, especially when you compare it with brilliant *Rigel* in Orion.

Yet another group of stars, even less common than the giants, are the *supergiants*. As the name suggests, they are of immense size. Both *Betelgeuse* and *Antares* belong to this group. *Betelgeuse* is a variable star in the sense that it changes its size. This is accompanied by a corresponding change in luminosity and hence in brightness. Think of *Betelgeuse* as an immense ball of diffuse gas which at its minimum would more than fill the Earth's orbit, and at maximum extend beyond the orbit of Mars. Being comparitively low in temperature, 3,100°K., *Betelgeuse* is reddish in colour.

More common than the giants and supergiants are the *white dwarfs*. They have an incredibly high density but are small in size and low in luminosity. The most well-known white dwarf is *Sirius B*, or the *Companion of Sirius*. Sirius is, in fact, a double star, and the star we call by that name should more rightly be called *Sirius A*.

The companion is intensely hot (11,200°K.) but of low luminosity (0.0008). This means that it is a body of planetary size, with a diameter only 0·022 that of the Sun. Yet its mass is almost equal to the Sun's, so that its density, or mass per unit volume, is incredibly high. Strange to say, *Sirius B* is 27,000 times more massive than the Sun. A cubic inch of its interior would weigh nearly a ton. Even more remarkable is the fact that another white dwarf, known as *van Maanen's Star*, has an average density 10 times that of *Sirius B*.

These groupings are of great significance in studies of the life histories of the stars and of their behaviour both as

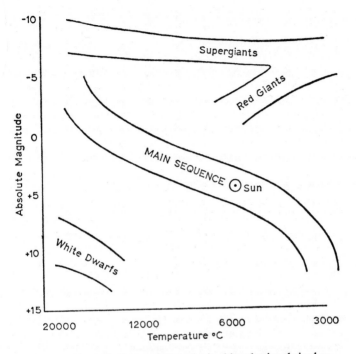

FIG. 15. The main classes of stars obtained by plotting their absolute magnitudes against their surface temperatures

individuals and as a population. They also reflect important differences in internal structure and the processes which keep the stars shining for thousands of millions of years. This aspect of astrophysics is perhaps the most exciting of all, and can be recommended as a field for private study by anyone who has a good knowledge of physics. The principles involved are now covered in most textbooks both at popular and more advanced levels.

A large number of stars, like *Betelgeuse*, vary in apparent brightness. The change in *Betelgeuse*, however, is semi-regular while that in several other groups of variable stars is regular. A well-known star of this latter type is *Beta Persei*, or *Algol*. It goes through its changes in brightness with great regularity. For about $2\frac{1}{2}$ days it appears to be almost constant in brightness with a magnitude of 2·2. Then for 5 hours it fades to reach a minimum magnitude of 3·5 and after another 5 hours regains its former brilliance. The interval between two successive minima, 2 days 21 hours in this case, is called the *period*. Find this star on your own and try to catch its upward or downward trend in brightness. See also if you can determine the time of one of its minima, then turn to the B.A.A. *Handbook* and check whether you were right or not. The *Handbook* gives the approximate times of the minima throughout the year. *Algol* is just about circumpolar as seen from London.

Algol is a binary star; it consists of not one star but two. It is, moreover, an *eclipsing binary*, for as the two stars travel round each other one partially eclipses the other. The eclipsing star is larger but less luminous than the partially eclipsed one, and this accounts for the periodic drop in overall brightness. It so happens that the planes of the orbits of these two stars are almost edge-on as seen from the Earth. Actually there are three stars in the Algol system, but the third star is so placed that it has no share in the eclipsing.

Regular variable stars are not by any means all of the eclipsing type. Some, like *Delta Cephei*, pulsate, or wax and wane in size in a regular way and, in so doing, wax and wane in brightness. See if you can detect the changes in *Delta Cephei*. They were first noticed in 1784 by the English astronomer Goodricke. At maximum it is a star of about 3rd magnitude. The brightness decreases by about 1 mag. in 3 days 19 hours and then rapidly increases to a maximum in 1 day $13\frac{1}{2}$ hours, so giving a period of nearly 5 days 9 hours.

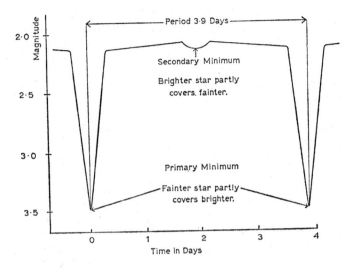

FIG. 16. Light-curve of Algol

Delta Cephei is the prototype of the large and important group of cepheid variable stars, or *cepheids*. Astronomers have discovered that there is a precise relationship between the period and luminosity for these stars. This means that if the period is known, so also is the luminosity. Knowing the luminosity and the apparent magnitude of the star, its distance can be found. Cepheids are therefore first-class indicators of distance. Thanks to them, astronomers have been able to extend the distance scale out to and beyond the distant stars of the Milky Way.

A completely different type of variable is *Omicron Ceti*, more generally known as *Mira*, which means 'the wonderful'. It was the first known variable, being discovered by Fabricius in August, 1596. Fabricius saw it first as a 3rd magnitude star, but a few months later it disappeared from view. In 1638 another astronomer, Holwarda, found that it became visible to the naked eye from time to time, while in between those times it was invisible, even in the telescope.

Mira Ceti is now classed as a long-period variable. Its average period is about 331 days, but it can vary from this by about plus or minus 8 days. The mag. at maximum is about 3·5 and at minimum 9·3: these are both average values.

While *Algol*, *Delta Cephei* and *Mira Ceti* are quite different in type, they are all easy objects for naked-eye observation. *Norton's Star Atlas* lists many more variables, but the great majority either go through a comparatively small change in brightness or drop below naked-eye visibility at and around their minima. The observation of these stars, especially the long-period variables which go through great changes in brightness, is a popular pursuit among amateur astronomers the world over. Looking them up is a first-class way of getting to know the fainter stars, and the light variations can be followed by making comparison estimates of their brightness. Work of this kind is organized and encouraged by the Variable Star Section of the B.A.A. It can provide complete instructions for the serious beginner, and prepares charts which give the positions and mags. of stars near the variable for comparison purposes.

In marked contrast to the regular or more-or-less regular brightening and fading of the main run of variable stars is the *nova* or *new star*. This appears quite suddenly, as if from nowhere, often rises to great brilliance, and then fades slowly into the obscurity from which it came. It is not newly created, however, as it may be found as a faint star on earlier photographs of the same part of the sky. Instead, it is a pre-existing star which, for reasons not yet thoroughly understood, has blown off its surface layers.

No two novae are alike, but they all show the rapid rise in brightness followed by a much more gradual fall. This behaviour was well shown by *Nova Persei 1901*, or the nova which appeared in the constellation of Perseus in 1901.

It was first detected by T. D. Anderson, a Scottish clergy-man, on February 21st of that year. He was on his way home on a clear night and, on looking in the direction of Perseus, noticed a new star of the 3rd magnitude. It so happened that astronomers at the Harvard College Observatory had photographed that part of the sky only two days before. When they received the news of Anderson's discovery they found the same star—but it was of the 13th mag. In two days, therefore, it had risen through 10 mags, or increased 10,000 times in luminosity. Maximum brilliance at zero mag. was reached about February 24th, after which it began to decrease, but at a much slower rate than it had increased. Three weeks after maximum, when the mag. was 4, a series of oscillations in brightness set in, but the star still continued to fade until 1912, when it stood at mag. 13 again.

Nova Aquila 1918 followed the same pattern but reached mag. −1·4 at maximum. Then came three others, with *Nova Herculis 1934* the brightest. Nova Herculis was my first sight of a nova. I well remember my satisfaction at being able to point it out to the family, friends and neighbours. I remember too how eagerly everyone accepted my invitation to look at the nova through a small telescope. They looked and saw—but it was just another star. I recall the interest aroused in astronomical circles when after rapidly reaching mag. 1·4 the star soon dropped to 2 and then oscillated up and down for several months as if uncertain what to do. The decline had, however, set in, and by May, 1935, the magnitude was down to about 12·5. But, biggest surprise of all, the star then recovered. It brightened to reach mag. 6, and only then decided to settle down to a long and steady second decline.

The brightest novae of all are the *supernovae*, or stars which literally blow themselves up. At their maxima they can reach a luminosity 10,000 times that of an average nova, or equal to that of 100,000,000 Suns. The brightest on record is *Supernova Cassiopeia 1572*, which rose to mag. −4 at

maximum and so appeared brighter than Venus. Discovered
by Tycho Brahe, and therefore often called 'Tycho's Star', its
appearance shattered the age-old belief that the stars were
unchanging and therefore eternal. At first it was thought to
be a fairly near object, but it kept to the one position relative
to other stars all through its 18 months appearance as a
naked-eye star. There could be no doubt whatever that it
was a change occurring in the sphere of fixed stars. It was,
however, universally accepted as a new star, for in those
times there was no evidence to the contrary. Many believed
that it was a second Star of Bethlehem—that it indicated
Christ's second coming and the terrors of the Apocalypse.
In this connection it is interesting to note that there is a
record of a nova appearing in 5 B.C., or about the time of
our Lord's birth. It was noticed by Chinese astronomers,
appeared in the constellation of Aquila, and lasted for about
70 days.

Another supernova, discovered by Kepler and often
called 'Kepler's Star', appeared in 1604. It rose rapidly in
brightness almost to rival Venus in splendour and then
gradually diminished until it disappeared early in 1606. Its
remains now form an intense source of radio waves. This
also applies to the supernova which blazed up in July, 1054.
It was recorded by Chinese and Japanese chroniclers as a
'guest' star. Its position near *Zeta Tauri* is now occupied by
an extremely faint object known as the Crab Nebula or M1
(Plate 8). Photographs of M1 taken with large telescopes show
that it is a vast mass of gas, complicated in structure and obviously in a state of tremendous turmoil. Near the centre
lie two faint but intensely hot stars from which the gases are
expanding at a speed of about 800 miles a second. On this
basis, and tracing them back to their origin, we find that the
explosion occurred about 900 years ago.

M1 is clearly the remains of the supernova of 1054, but
since its distance is estimated at 4,000 light-years, the
explosion took place some time about 3000 B.C. Modern

photographs of M1 therefore show it as it was about 2000 B.C.

The study of variable stars, as you will have already realized, is a study in itself. The name also applies to the study of any one group of variable stars, and some astronomers have devoted much time and attention to just one star alone. Peculiar stars, or stars that behave in an erratic way, are interesting not only in themselves but also as reminders that many stars, like people, have strong individual characteristics. They do not conform to the main sequence or to any other sequence. They produce the unexpected from time to time as if rebelling against attempts by astronomers to fit them into a general scheme with its predictable pattern of behaviour. There are, for example, stars like *RS Ophiuchi* and *U Scorpii* which explode not once but several times, so earning them the name *recurrent novae*. Then there are *U Geminorum*, *SS Cygni* and many other similar stars which flare up at irregular intervals, and others like *Z Camelopardalis*, *R Coronae Borealis*, *Gamma Cassiopeiae* and *RR Tauri* which are completely erratic in light behaviour. Most of them have been subjected to careful and regular study only in recent years, so you can well imagine how difficult it is to build up a picture of their life histories. This is a difficult-enough task with main-sequence stars which seem to have fairly regular habits, let alone with the queer types. It is, however, abundantly evident that the stars are changing things—that they change in size, temperature, luminosity, mass and every other attribute. Far from being eternal, as was thought some four centuries ago, the domain of the stars is one of constant change and immense variety.

Another thing that the beginner must get used to is the fact that many of the stars are not single objects but consist of two, three, four or even more stars. They look single to the naked eye, but are found to be otherwise when examined in a telescope.

We have already mentioned *Alpha Centauri*, *61 Cygni*,

Sirius and *Algol* in this connection, although it should be said straightway that no telescope shows *Algol* as three stars. But first to be quite clear about the difference between *optical doubles* and *binaries*. An optical double occurs when two stars at a great difference in distance from us happen to be in almost the same direction. They appear side by side, so giving the impression that they are close together in space. In a binary, however, the two stars *are* close together in space, being associated through the invisible ties of gravitation. They accordingly revolve round one another as a waltzing pair. Whether they can be seen as two will depend on their distance from the Earth and their separation, or distance apart. These features decide their angular separation, and the smaller this is the larger must be the telescope which will show them as two separate stars.

The unaided human eye can usually *resolve* a double star, or distinguish two stars as two if they are about equal in magnitude and not less than 1 minute of arc apart. A well-known naked-eye double star is *Mizar*, or *Zeta Ursae Majoris*, the middle star in the handle of the Plough. Its companion is *Alcor*, the faint star nearby. Yet if *Mizar* is examined through a small telescope or pair of binoculars it will be seen to be not one star but two. In this case the two stars have an angular separation of about 14″, or 14 seconds of arc, which explains why they cannot be seen as two by the unaided eye. The brighter of the two stars is itself double, but cannot be seen as two even in the 200-inch Palomar telescope, the largest telescope in the world. The discovery was made in 1889 by Miss Maury when she examined some spectrograms of *Mizar*. Certain lines in the spectrograms were periodically doubled, thereby revealing that one of the two stars was itself double (Plate 9). The period came out at about 21 days, and the star became known as a *spectroscopic binary*. In the same year the German astronomer Vogel found a similar change in spectrograms of *Algol*. It too was a spectroscopic binary, thereby confirming the suggestion

Plate 13. A Spiral Galaxy in Andromeda (Lick Observatory)

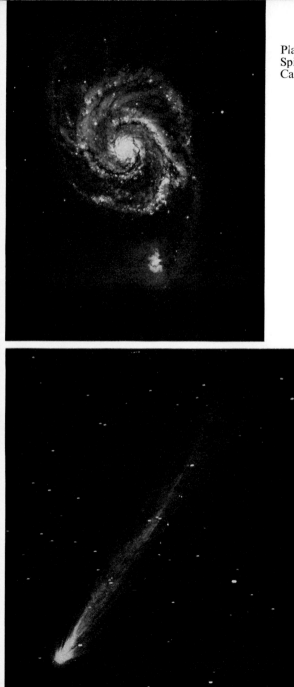

Plate 14.
Spiral Nebula in
Canes Venatici

Plate 15.
The Comet
Morehouse, 1908
(Royal Greenwich
Observatory)

made earlier by Goodricke that *Algol*'s light variations were due to the periodic partial eclipse of one star by another.

While the brighter component of *Mizar* is therefore a spectroscopic binary, *Algol* is both a spectroscopic binary and an eclipsing binary. In the case of *Mizar* the two stars have their orbits so arranged to our line of sight that partial eclipses cannot possibly occur.

Another well-known naked-eye double star is *Epsilon Lyrae;* the two stars are separated by over 3 minutes of arc. Yet the telescope shows each star as two, thereby providing us with a 'double-double'. Nearby is bright *Vega*, which forms an optical double with a 10th mag. star nearly 1 minute of arc away. Other naked-eye doubles are *Theta Tauri* and *Alpha Capricorni*, but you will find these and several more in the lists of double stars in *Norton's Star Atlas*.

Norton gives the names, positions, mags., angles of position and angular separations of several hundred double stars. If you possess a small telescope you will get much pleasure in looking them up in the sky. As a general rule a 1-inch-aperture telescope will resolve or divide a double star of separation 5 seconds of arc. A 2-inch extends this to 2·5″ while a 3-inch can reach to about 1·5″.

Anyone who gives the night sky more than a casual glance cannot fail to be impressed by the Milky Way. This is particularly so in the northern summer when the sky is clear and the Moon absent, for the Milky Way then parades some of its brightest parts. At midnight at that time of the year it arches across the sky from north to south, with its brightest parts appearing in Cygnus through to Sagittarius in the south. It again runs from north to south at midnight in mid-winter, but with the fainter regions of Perseus and Auriga making it appear much less conspicuous than in summer. Its general form is traced on the Philips' Planisphere, and by studying this (and, of course, the real thing

G

in the sky itself) you will be able to see how it changes its aspect both in a night and throughout the year.

The telescope shows that the Milky Way is made up of myriads of stars, all so faint that they cannot be seen as single objects by the unaided eye. It shows too that the patchiness in the Milky Way arises from the way the stars are distributed. In the bright parts they are thickly carpeted, whereas in the darker parts they are but thinly scattered. Photographs of regions of Cygnus through to Sagittarius show great fields of stars and many areas where the stars appear almost to be piled one beside another. They also show dark irregular patches, which when viewed together with the star fields give the whole a patchy appearance. The dark patches are due to clouds of *interstellar dust* that lie between the stars and us. These clouds cut off the light of the more distant stars, so blocking out our view of the starry regions beyond. The stars which we do see in these dark wastes are mostly foreground stars, or stars that lie between us and the dust clouds.

It is important to realize that if we stay all the time in any one place we see only about one-half of the Milky Way. In its full extent it girdles the sphere of stars, and its southern reaches are every bit as beautiful as the northern. From Sagittarius it runs with great brilliance through Scorpius, Norma, Circinus, Centaurus, Crux and Carina, but grows fainter through Vela, Puppis, Canis Major and Gemini through to Cassiopeia. A striking feature in the north is the dark space called the Great Rift. It lies between Cygnus and Sagittarius, dividing the main course of the Milky Way into two streams. A striking feature in the south is the dark space called the Coalsack. Located near the Southern Cross, it is roughly oval and made the more conspicuous by being surrounded by faint stars. The comparative emptiness of these regions, as in others, arises not from a real paucity of stars but from the obscuring action of vast clouds of interstellar dust.

Since the Milky Way forms almost a complete circle round the sky, astronomers often refer to the great circle that follows it most closely as the *galactic circle*. The points 90° from this are the *north galactic pole*, located in Coma Berenices, and *south galactic pole*, located in Sculptor. But is the Milky Way in its nature a ring or circle of stars? The answer is most emphatically, no. It is an optical effect—an effect of perspective.

Suppose the stars were evenly scattered throughout space and that they formed a great ball with the Sun in the middle. The whole night sky would then be aglow with the faint background light of innumerable faint stars. The Milky Way would then cover the entire sky. Now imagine that the ball is considerably flattened, so that it becomes more like a watch in shape, but keep the Sun in the middle. From this central position more stars will be seen in the direction of the rim than in directions at right angles to the rim. This would bring about the effect of a misty band of light, but the Milky Way so produced would be uniform in width and brightest in the middle of its course. The true state of affairs is very different from this, but the second model is a step in the right direction, and it does explain what we mean when we say that the Milky Way is an effect of perspective.

A model much nearer the truth is one in which the stars form a flattened system with the Sun located close to the central plane but well removed from the centre. The system, called the *Milky Way System*, or the *Galaxy*, has no definite boundaries, for the stars just thin out around its 'edges', but the overall shape is round and flat. The stars are not uniformly distributed, but are more highly concentrated in and around the galactic plane and towards the centre. At the centre lies an almost ball-like mass of highly luminous giant stars. This constitutes the hub or *nucleus* of the system, but even at this central bulge the thickness of the system is still far less than its overall diameter. The nucleus lies in the direction of Sagittarius. Yet we cannot see it, for it is hidden from view by obscuring clouds of dust.

The Milky Way System is so vast that the distance across its diameter is of the order of 80,000 light-years. The Sun is about 27,000 light-years from the centre, or about two-thirds the distance from the centre to the edge. The naked-eye view of the night sky, and taking into account both its northern and southern aspects, is therefore an extremely limited view of that part of the Galaxy in which the Sun resides. The other far larger part we shall never see, for it lies beyond the nucleus which is itself obscured from view. The stars in the Milky Way are therefore thousands and tens of thousands of light-years away, while bright stars like *Vega, Deneb, Castor, Pollux* and many others are comparatively near neighbours to the Sun which happen to have the Milky Way as their background. So great are interstellar distances, and so small the stars in comparison, that two neighbouring stars in the Galaxy are separated by millions and millions of miles. They are like two flies roaming freely on the Isle of Wight—they have all that room at their disposal. Or, as the late Sir James Jeans once wrote, six specks of dust in Waterloo Station about represent the extent to which space is occupied by stars in its most crowded parts.

So far we have given the impression that the Galaxy is a static system—that the stars are fixed in space once and for all time. The wonderful thing is, that instead of being fixed, the stars whirl round the centre of the Galaxy. Not one star is at rest. The entire Galaxy is rotating, which is why it is a highly flattened system. The Sun and the stars near it travel at the terrific pace of 140 miles a second. Yet so vast are the distances involved that the Sun takes about 200,000,000 years for one complete journey. Since the estimated age of the Sun is about 5,000,000,000 years, this means that it has as yet made only 25 trips round the galactic centre.

If the Sun travels at this speed then are not stars at twice its distance, or 54,000 light-years from the galactic centre, travelling at 280 miles a second? Fortunately for the stability of the system, the stars do not go round together as if fixed to the spokes of a gigantic spinning wheel. Instead, and like the planets in the solar system, those nearest the centre move

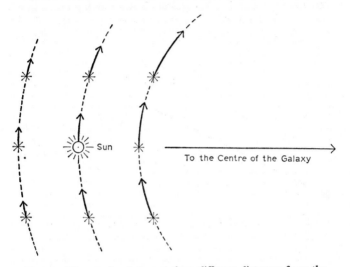

Fig. 17. The speeds of stars at three different distances from the centre of the Galaxy

faster than those further away. This means that from our position on the Earth, stars near the Sun but further out from the centre than we are appear to lag behind, while those nearer the centre appear to forge ahead.

Think of the Galaxy not as a more-or-less uniform disk of fixed stars but as a giant, spinning Catherine wheel. It has a definite spiral structure, rather like that of a Catherine wheel but much less regular. Stars, gas and dust combine to form *spiral arms*, or knotted and curved streams of immense extent. The Sun and its neighbours reside in a cluster of stars in part of a huge spiral arm which is just one of a whole system of spiral arms. All the naked-eye stars belong to a local cluster or knot in one of the spiral arms of the Galaxy.

The stars of the night sky, and of the daytime one too, are therefore moving suns viewed from a moving Earth which travels round a moving Sun. Small wonder then that the sky is gradually changing in appearance, but so slowly that we

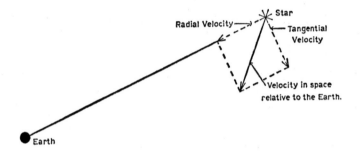

FIG. 18. The two components of a star's velocity in space relative to the Earth

cannot in a lifetime detect any change by naked-eye observation. That individual stars *are* moving is shown by studies of their positions relative to one another. More than two centuries ago Edmond Halley discovered that *Sirius, Aldebaran* and *Arcturus* had apparently moved from their positions as given in star catalogues made some 2,000 years earlier. Since his time, and using special techniques, astronomers have detected movements in a very large number of stars. The angular distance which a star covers in a year is called its *proper motion*. Knowing this, and the distance of the star, it is an easy matter to find its cross motion or *tangential velocity* in miles per second. This is not, however, its actual motion in space, for it is probably travelling in a direction towards or away from us. To determine the motion in space astronomers have also to measure the star's *radial velocity*, or its velocity towards or away from us. This is done by studying the star's spectrogram. The tangential velocity and the radial velocity are the two component velocities of the resultant velocity in space. So knowing them both, astronomers can determine both the actual velocity in space and its direction.

The study of the proper motions of a large number of nearby stars shows that the Sun is travelling at a speed of 12 miles a second towards a point in the constellation of Hercules. This motion is only a relative one, however, for the stars are themselves moving round the galactic centre. Relative to that centre the Sun and its nearby companions are travelling at a speed of 140 miles a second, and the direction ahead is not in Hercules but in Cygnus.

The story of how astronomers have built up our knowledge of the Galaxy is one of the most fascinating chapters in the whole history of astronomy. You should lose no time in reading about it all—about the work done in this field by Sir William Herschel, Kapteyn, Shapley, Oort, Baade, and many others, about the way ideas have changed, especially in the last 50 years, and how radio-astronomy in recent times has probed into regions hitherto hidden from view by the clouds of interstellar dust. You will find that whereas astronomers about 60 years ago thought that the Galaxy contained all the stars in the Universe, they now know that it is just one galaxy among myriads of others.

7

Stars, Gas and Dust

FROM time to time astronomers have noticed hazy-looking stars in the sky. Some of these have turned out to be comets, but others have kept a fixed position among the stars. In 1612, for example, the German astronomer Simon Marius drew attention to a tiny misty patch in the constellation of Andromeda. When he examined it through a telescope it still looked misty, and he compared its appearance to that of a candle flame seen through a piece of horn. Then in 1656 the Dutch astronomer Christian Huygens discovered a hazy star in the sword of Orion, and this too looked misty when examined through a telescope. These nebulous-looking objects or *nebulae* increased in number as the telescope grew in size and power, and by 1784 had reached 103 in number. This last list was provided by the French astronomer Charles Messier. His main interest in the sky, and in life also, was comets. While searching for them he came across so many nebulae that could be mistaken for comets that he decided to list them all. They were, for him, things of nuisance value only, although he did suggest that astronomers should study them for possible signs of change.

The nebulae listed by Messier still bear his name: they are given the designation M followed by their position in Messier's catalogue. The nebula in Andromeda, for instance, is M13, or the 13th object in Messier's list, while the one in Orion is M42. The full list of Messier nebulae is given in *Olcott's Field Book of the Skies*, 4th edn., 1954. When Sir

William Herschel explored the northern sky with large reflecting telescopes he discovered several thousand nebulae, and his son, Sir John Herschel, discovered thousands more in the southern sky. These nebulae, which include the Messier objects, are now referred to by the letters NGC (New General Catalogue) followed by a catalogue number. This means that M13 is also referred to as NGC224 and M42 as NGC1976. The New General Catalogue, revised by J. L. E. Dreyer who also prepared additional Index Catalogues, is available in its complete form from the Royal Astronomical Society, London.

The number of objects listed in these catalogues runs into many thousands, but comparatively few are essentially nebulous. The great majority are galaxies, or systems of stars like the Galaxy or Milky Way System. The rest belong to the Galaxy, or at least lie near it, and fall into one of three categories: *open star clusters*, *globular star clusters* and *gaseous nebulae*. Of these only the gaseous nebulae are essentially nebulous and therefore really merit the name nebulae.

A good example of an open star cluster is the group known as the *Pleiades* (Plate 10). We have already referred to it, and the enthusiastic reader will by now have found it for himself. On a clear night the Pleiades show 7 stars to the unaided eye but some observers claim to have seen as many as 14 stars. Binoculars or a small telescope will certainly reveal many more, while large telescopes show many hundreds. The group covers an area slightly larger than the apparent area of the Moon. It is therefore seen at its best with low magnifications and correspondingly wide angular fields of view.

As a boy, and soon after I had 'discovered' the Pleiades, I marked down as many stars as I could on paper. I did this several times, for it was good training in drawing at the telescope. My final map agreed quite favourably with a chart of the Pleiades which I came across later. The group has always fascinated me, but the thrill of seeing it for the first time both with the naked eye and through a telescope was unique. I still regard the Pleiades with something akin to affection, and the knowledge that they consist of a family of about 500 stars, all travelling together in the same direction through space, in no way affects this view. They are at an estimated distance of 350 light-years, which makes them a comparatively near group. Their main stars are all much larger and more luminous than the Sun.

Associated with the Pleiades are clouds of dust which shine by reflecting and scattering the light of the extremely luminous stars nearby. This *reflection nebulosity*, as it is called, was first seen in 1859 by the astronomer Tempel as a faint glow near the star *Merope*. Modern photographs reveal that all the main stars of the Pleiades are involved in veils of nebulosity—that they are like, as Tennyson described them, 'a swarm of fireflies tangled in a silver braid'.

Another open star cluster, the *Hyades*, also lies in the constellation of Taurus. It too is best seen under low magnifying powers, for being nearer to us than the Pleiades it covers a much larger area. The distance across the cluster is about 50 light-years and its centre is approximately 120 light-years away. The great majority of its stars are red giants. The reddish star *Aldebaran*, however, is not a member of the group. It so happens that *Aldebaran* lies about half-way between us and the Hyades and therefore *appears* to be one along with them.

Other open star clusters easily seen with the unaided eye and well worth looking at with binoculars are *Praesepe*, or 'The Beehive' in Cancer, and the 'Double Cluster' in Perseus. Norton gives the positions of many more, some of them so distant that a small telescope will fail to resolve them into stars. It is interesting to know that the five middle stars of The Plough are part of a star cluster which is almost on our doorstep as star clusters go. These five are about 70 light-years away and are all travelling in the same direction through space. The two end stars, not members of the group, are travelling in different directions. So in thousands of years' time The Plough will no longer look anything like a plough. *Sirius*, strange to say, is a member of the group, and at its distance of nearly 9 light-years accentuates the fact that the cluster is a near one.

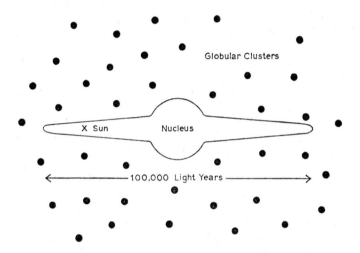

Globular Clusters

X Sun   Nucleus

←————— 100,000 Light Years —————→

FIG. 19. Section through the Galaxy and system of globular clusters

A star cluster of quite a different kind is M13 in Hercules. The naked eye on a clear night sees it as a faint hazy star about one-third of the way from *Eta Herculis* to *Zeta Herculis*. A small telescope will still show it as a hazy star, but larger instruments reveal that it is a swarm of stars almost circular in outline. Photographs with giant telescopes show thousands of stars which gradually thin out in number away from the centre. M13 is, in fact, a ball-like swarm of stars called a *globular star cluster;* the apparent high concentration of stars near the centre is largely an effect of perspective. Its distance is estimated at 14,000 light-years, which places it far beyond even the faintest stars in Hercules. Its stars are intensely hot and highly luminous. When you see M13 just think that the light entering your eye left on its long journey about 14,000 years ago. What is M13 like now? Probably almost the same as it was then, for 14,000 years in the life of a community of stars is like a second in the life of Man.

Another fine globular cluster, and one even more splendid than M13, is *Omega Centauri*. It lies in the southern hemisphere of the sky and is about one-third of the way from *Zeta Centauri* to *Gamma Centauri*. Originally listed as a star, the telescope shows that it consists of thousands of stars. Altogether about 200 globular clusters have been found. They avoid the region of the Milky Way, but this is because they are there hidden behind the great clouds of cosmic dust. They lie *beyond* the stars of the Milky Way. Considered as a group all the globular star clusters form a ball-like cluster far larger than the Galaxy. The Galaxy, then, must be regarded as lying inside an extremely thin haze or halo of globular clusters. And what is true for our spiral Galaxy holds for several others and probably for most if not all other spiral galaxies.

M42, the nebula discovered by Huygens, is now called the Great Nebula in Orion (Plate 11). It is a gaseous nebula, for it consists largely of an irregular mass of glowing gas. The gas is made to glow by the intensely hot stars embedded in it; it absorbs their short-wave radiation and re-emits it at longer wavelengths. The gas itself is extremely thin and covers an immense volume of space. The remarkable thing is that the Great Nebula is just a tiny part, although the brightest part, of a vast complex of gas and dust that extends over the entire constellation of Orion. M43, another gaseous nebula slightly south of M42, can therefore be regarded as part of this complex.

Just over a century ago many astronomers thought that M42 was just another cluster of stars, but one so distant that not even the largest telescopes of those times could resolve it into stars. In 1864, however, Sir William Huggins analysed its light with a spectroscope and found that it consisted not of stars but of glowing gas. He found that several other nebulae had a similar nature, and we now know that they are extremely plentiful, especially in the region of the Milky Way (Plate 12). They all belong to our Galaxy and those in Messier's catalogue are comparatively near objects. The Great Nebula in Orion, by far the most conspicuous of its type, is estimated to be about 900 light-years away.

There is now ample evidence to show that only a small part of the mass or quantity of matter in the Galaxy is in the form of stars. By far the larger part consists of interstellar gas and dust. These are concentrated in and around the galactic plane to form a kind of cosmic haze, although the gas itself is almost transparent. Here and there, where it surrounds very hot stars, the gas shines and lies revealed as a gaseous nebula. Here and there the dust reflects the light of the stars, as in the case of the Pleiades, and is seen as a reflection nebula. But the dust is the real villain of the piece. Its presence in the haze both dims and reddens the light of very distant stars, while local concentrations in the form of giant clouds cut off our view altogether. The dust is by no means uniformly distributed in space, which adds to the difficulty of allowing for its effects when studying distant stars in the Milky Way.

Dust clouds which show a fairly definite form are called *dark nebulae*. The Coalsack is a good example. It appears prominent mainly because it is comparatively near to us (about 500 light-years) and therefore has hardly any foreground stars projected on to it. If it were 10 times further away, however, we should hardly notice it at all. There would then be so many stars between us and it that its dark surface would be covered with numerous stars; it might then look like a fairly bright part of the Milky Way.

The term 'dust' suggests the tiny particles we gather up in a vacuum cleaner. Interstellar dust is quite different; the particles are extremely small and are probably tiny crystals of frozen gases. In the Sun's neighbourhood there are probably between 1 and 100 dust particles per cubic mile. The contents of a volume of interstellar space as large as the Earth would therefore weigh only 2 pounds. Yet so vast are interstellar distances that even at this density the dust can dim and sometimes block out the light of very distant stars.

People sometimes ask how far they can see. If they have good eyesight, and without using a telescope or binoculars, they can see an object about 12,000,000,000,000 miles away. The object in question is M31, once thought to be a gaseous nebula belonging to our Galaxy but now known to be another galaxy. It is usually referred to as the Great Spiral Galaxy in Andromeda. It lies slightly north of the star *Mu Andromedae*, being in almost direct line with that star and *Beta Andromedae*. It is therefore high up in the sky for northern observers at midnight in early October, and lies well clear of the dust clouds in the Milky Way.

To the unaided eye M31 is a small misty patch of light. It still looks hazy in a small telescope, but is then seen to have an elongated shape. Only by photographing it with giant telescopes can it be shown for what it is—a vast, flattened complex of stars, gas and dust similar in form and structure to our own Galaxy.

M31 is at an estimated distance of nearly 2,000,000 light-years. This clearly places it far beyond the stars of the Milky Way. It appears small and hazy because of its immense distance. It appears oval in shape because its plane is slightly tilted towards us. Viewed face-on it would appear round: viewed edge-on it would look spindle-shaped. In brief, it is similar to our own Galaxy in both content, shape and structure. It is, however, slightly larger in size, the distance across it being about 100,000 light-years compared with

80,000 light-years for the Galaxy. You may wonder why it looks so small, at least to the unaided eye. This is because the eye sees only its brighter central parts. The photographic plate can register much more, but even this fails to record the extremely faint outlying regions. By using sensitive photoelectric devices attached to large telescopes astronomers have traced M31 over a distance of about $7\frac{1}{2}°$ or 15 times the apparent diameter of the Moon. If, therefore, we represent the Galaxy by a sixpence, M31 would be represented by a shilling about 18 inches away from the sixpence.

Detailed studies of photographs of M31 show the spiral arms outlined by interstellar dust clouds and peppered with stars, clusters of stars and bright gaseous nebulae. The photographs show part of the great starry nucleus and enable astronomers to identify occasional supernovae, different types of stars and part of the surrounding halo of globular clusters. Spectrograms of M31 show that it is rotating, and in a way similar to our own Galaxy. Indeed it is so similar to the Galaxy in all respects that it ranks almost as its twin.

The two nearest galaxies are the Magellanic Clouds. They lie in southern skies and can be seen on a clear night with the eyes alone. They look like two bits of the Milky Way broken loose. Each one contains the usual ingredients— stars, gas and dust. Their distance, approximately 170,000 light-years, has been established mainly by studying the cepheids in them and applying the known relationship between cepheid period and luminosity. Irregular in shape, they show no definite spiral form, and being much smaller than the Galaxy can be regarded as two satellites or companion galaxies. M31 also has two companions, but these are quite symmetrical in shape and show no signs of dust clouds and the associated spiral structure.

Just as the stars differ among themselves so do the galaxies. Some, like the Magellanic Clouds, are irregular in form and shape and have no special structure. Others, called *elliptical galaxies,* have an oval appearance but show no signs of a spiral structure. Then there are the spiral galaxies (Plates 13 and 14), with the Galaxy and M31 representing the normal type. Like the stars, galaxies also have a great range in size— they have their giants and their dwarfs. They also form groups or clusters. The Galaxy, the Magellanic Clouds, and M31 with its two companions belong to the so-called *Local Group.* But while the *Local Group* contains only about 16 members, other clusters contain several hundreds.

Clusters of galaxies are the largest known physical units in existence. The galaxies themselves are strewn out to as far as telescopes, both optical and radio, can probe. Their numbers may well be without limit, for every increase in the space-penetrating power of telescopes so far has resulted in additions to the known number of galaxies. They appear in all parts of the sky with the exception of around the galactic plane, where in the main they are hidden behind the galactic dust clouds. This gives the illusion that the Galaxy is at the centre of the realm of galaxies, but it is only an illusion. They would appear in a similar way from a position in any other galaxy.

The 200-inch telescope on Palomar Mountain can reach out to several thousand million galaxies, and to distances of the order of 5,000,000,000 light-years. On the basis of our model in which 2,000,000 light-years was represented by 18 inches, the most distant galaxy photographed so far would be about three-quarters of a mile away. This observable region, with the Galaxy appearing to be in the middle, is sometimes referred to as the *Universe.* But the word is more usually applied to the observable domain plus the part as yet to be discovered. This larger whole has no centre and no edge. As seen from any one viewpoint the galaxies will appear to be scattered out in all directions. In brief, any one galaxy is the centre of the Universe. It appears that astronomers have as yet surveyed only a tiny part of something, call it the Cosmos, the Universe or what you will, which is far larger than the observable domain. Of course, different points of view give rise to different kinds of Universe, and if the word is to be used at all it should be defined beforehand.

The study of the age, extent and nature of the physical Universe as a whole is known as *cosmology*. This is obviously a study in itself, and one which has deep roots in both astronomy and philosophy. An associated subject is *cosmogony*, or the study of the origin of the physical Universe as a whole and in its various parts. Both subjects have been the concern of astronomy for the greater part of its history. The astronomy of the Sumerians, Ancient Egyptians, Ancient Greeks and other early peoples was largely a mixture of cosmology and cosmogony. They found, and to their evident satisfaction, a picture of the Universe which was at once aesthetically pleasing and intellectually satisfying. The picture was, however, essentially geocentric, or Earth-centred, and it remained so right up to and even beyond the time of Copernicus. You will find the history of cosmology a fascinating subject, although heavy going in several places, for it embraces aspects of astronomy, philosophy, history, theology, physics and mathematics. The field has been well covered by various authors, but the best way to approach it is to read one or more books on the general history of astronomy.

Realizing these things, you will appreciate my surprise on receiving a letter from a schoolboy who asked for information about the Universe. His teacher had made this the subject of a week-end essay for homework. On another occasion a boy wrote in to say that he wanted to become a cosmologist. Could I tell him how he could become one?

Almost every book on general astronomy ends on the topic of the origin and expansion of the Universe. There is no need to repeat the information here, but a few words of caution will be all to the good. The topic is by its very nature one for the specialist. Popular expositions deal of necessity

H

with the broad outlines in terms that the layman can understand. These terms do not necessarily have the same meaning for scientists as they do for the layman. For example, we usually associate space with volume, as when we remark that a caged bird lives in a confined space. We may perhaps think of it as a distance (e.g. 'the space in between'), as the absence of matter even in its most finely divided form (e.g. 'the vacuum of outer space') or as something to be conquered (e.g. 'the conquest of space'). At all events, we regard it as a permanent feature of the world around us, as a thing in itself, with its own physical and geometrical properties. The latter are such that the shortest distance between two points is a straight line, two parallel lines meet at infinity, the angles of a triangle add up to 180° and so on. The world of science, however, regards space as a concept, or creation of the mind. As such, it can be given all manner of properties. For instance, it can transmit the Sun's heat without itself being heated; it can be flat, curved, distorted, empty, filled with lines of magnetic force, ether and particles; it can be such that the shortest distance between two points is not a straight line, two parallel lines do not meet at infinity, and the angles of a triangle do not add up to 180°. The scientist is therefore free to arrange, adapt and alter the concept as he pleases, but since it must be a useful weapon in his mental armoury he makes it fit experience.

In the same way time, matter, mass, energy, atoms and the Universe are concepts: they have one meaning in everyday life but in scientific thinking (and therefore in a subject like cosmology) require defining before they are used at all. Ideally, to understand the ideas of modern cosmology even at a semi-popular level is to understand the nature and purpose of science, to appreciate its particular methods, scope, limitations and philosophy, and to know something of its history. This is a tall order, but then cosmology is a specialist subject.

A good rule in your reading will be to keep the observational bases of the knowledge constantly in focus. Instead of worrying whether the Universe is expanding, for example, think instead of the observed shift in the lines of spectrograms of distant galaxies. These shifts are surely the crux of the matter, for they belong to experience—you can see them and measure them. But nobody has as yet measured the rate at which the Universe is expanding, nor can we see it expanding. It depends also on what you mean by 'the Universe'. Opinions differ, but everyone agrees that there are shifts in the lines of spectrograms of distant galaxies. In brief, try to distinguish between fact and theory. Beware too of inventions like the 'cosmological principle' and 'perfect cosmological principle'; they are not inviolable rules discovered by Man, but inventions in the mind of Man. Regard the idea of the 'Primeval Atom' with more than a pinch of salt—it's just part of a theory and is no more fact than the tiny electrons which are supposed to revolve round the nuclei of atoms. These things belong to mental constructs called 'models' which scientists devise in order to describe their observations. If, owing to some discovery or new observation, the facts no longer fit the model it is discarded. As the years pass, more and more models are either thrown out of the structure of science or adapted to meet the new conditions. Which explains why members of the public sometimes complain that astronomers cannot make up their minds. As one lady once remarked to me: 'Why don't astronomers measure the speed at which the Universe expands and be done with it?'

These comments will, I hope, encourage rather than deter you from reading in this field. That which is only partly seen and a little understood always presents us with the challenge of finding out more and acquiring a better understanding. This is true not just in cosmology but in every aspect of astronomy. One often gets the impression that we know practically everything about, say, the Moon, whereas in truth a great deal more remains to be discovered. The whole subject of astronomy is a challenge, and one as great now as it has ever been. If you sense something of the challenge that the sky makes to you as an individual and feel encouraged to accept it after reading these pages, then my efforts have been more than worth while.

Appendix I

THE CONSTELLATIONS

Name	Genitive Form	English Equivalent
Andromeda	Andromedae	Andromeda
Antlia	Antliae	The Air Pump
Apus	Apodis	The Bird of Paradise
Aquarius	Aquarii	The Water Carrier
Aquila	Aquilae	The Eagle
Ara	Arae	The Altar
Aries	Arietis	The Ram
Auriga	Aurigae	The Charioteer
Boötes	Boötis	The Herdsman
Caelum	Caeli	The Graving Tool
Camelopardus	Camelopardalis	The Giraffe
Cancer	Cancri	The Crab
Canes Venatici	Canum Venaticorum	The Hunting Dogs
Canis Major	Canis Majoris	The Great Dog
Canis Minor	Canis Minoris	The Little Dog
Capricornus	Capricorni	The Capricorn
Carina	Carinae	The Keel
Cassiopeia	Cassiopeiae	Cassiopeia
Centaurus	Centauri	The Centaur
Cepheus	Cephei	Cepheus
Cetus	Ceti	The Whale
Chamaeleon	Chamaeleontis	The Chamaeleon
Circinus	Circini	The Pair of Compasses
Columba	Columbae	The Dove
Coma Berenices	Comae Berenices	Berenices' Hair
Corona Australis	Coronae Australis	The Southern Crown
Corona Borealis	Coronae Borealis	The Northern Crown
Corvus	Corvi	The Crow

Name	Genitive Form	English Equivalent
Crater	Crateris	The Cup
Crux	Crucis	The Cross
Cygnus	Cygni	The Swan
Delphinus	Delphini	The Dolphin
Dorado	Doradus	The Swordfish
Draco	Draconis	The Dragon
Equuleus	Equulei	The Little Horse
Eridanus	Eridani	The River Eridanus
Fornax	Fornacis	The Furnace
Gemini	Geminorum	The Twins
Grus	Gruis	The Crane
Hercules	Herculis	Hercules
Horologium	Horologii	The Clock
Hydra	Hydrae	The Sea Serpent
Hydrus	Hydri	The Water Snake
Indus	Indi	The Indian
Lacerta	Lacertae	The Lizard
Leo	Leonis	The Lion
Leo Minor	Leonis Minoris	The Little Lion
Lepus	Leporis	The Hare
Libra	Librae	The Scales
Lupus	Lupi	The Wolf
Lynx	Lyncis	The Lynx
Lyra	Lyrae	The Lyre
Mensa	Mensae	The Table Mountain
Microscopium	Microscopii	The Microscope
Monoceros	Monocerotis	The Unicorn
Musca	Muscae	The Fly
Norma	Normae	The Ruler
Octans	Octantis	The Octant
Ophiuchus	Ophiuchi	The Serpent Bearer
Orion	Orionis	Orion
Pavo	Pavonis	The Peacock
Pegasus	Pegasi	Pegasus
Perseus	Persei	Perseus
Phoenix	Phoenicis	The Phoenix
Pictor	Pictoris	The Painter
Pisces	Piscium	The Fishes

Name	Genitive Form	English Equivalent
Piscis Australis	Piscis Australis	The Southern Fish
Puppis	Puppis	The Poop
Pyxis	Pyxidis	The Mariner's Compass
Reticulum	Reticuli	The Net
Sagitta	Sagittae	The Arrow
Sagittarius	Sagittarii	The Archer
Scorpio	Scorpii	The Scorpion
Sculptor	Sculptoris	The Sculptor
Scutum	Scuti	The Shield
Serpens	Serpentis	The Serpent
Sextans	Sextantis	The Sextant
Taurus	Tauri	The Bull
Telescopium	Telescopii	The Telescope
Triangulum	Trianguli	The Triangle
Triangulum Australis	Trianguli Australis	The Southern Triangle
Tucana	Tucanae	The Toucan
Ursa Major	Ursae Majoris	The Great Bear
Ursa Minor	Ursae Minoris	The Little Bear
Vela	Velorum	The Sails
Virgo	Virginis	The Virgin
Volans	Volantis	The Flying Fish
Vulpecula	Vulpeculae	The Fox

Appendix II

THE GREEK ALPHABET

Letter	Name	Letter	Name
α	Alpha	ν	Nu
β	Beta	ξ	Xi
γ	Gamma	ο	Omicron
δ	Delta	π	Pi
ε	Epsilon	ρ	Rho
ζ	Zeta	σ	Sigma
η	Eta	τ	Tau
θ	Theta	υ	Upsilon
ι	Iota	φ	Phi
κ	Kappa	χ	Chi
λ	Lambda	ψ	Psi
μ	Mu	ω	Omega

Appendix III

THE TWENTY BRIGHTEST STARS

Name	R.A. h m	Decl. ° '	Mag. apparent visual	Mag. absolute visual	Luminosity (Sun=1)	Distance (light-years)
Sirius	6 42·9	−16 39	−1·5	+1·36	26	8·7
Canopus	6 22·8	−52 40	−0·7	−7·4	80,000	300
α Centauri	14 36·2	−60 38	0·3	+4·7, +6·1	1·12, 0·32	4
Vega	18 35·2	+38 44	0·0	+0·6	50	26
Capella	5 13·0	+45 57	0·1	−0·6	150	45
Arcturus	14 13·4	+19 26	0·1	−0·2	100	36
Rigel	5 12·2	−8 15	0·1	−5·8	18,000	850
Procyon	7 36·7	+5 21	0·3	+2·8	5·4	11
Achernar	1 35·9	−57 29	0·5	−0·9	200	75
β Centauri	14 00·3	−60 08	0·6	−3·8	3,100	300
Altair	19 48·3	+8 44	0·8	+2·4	9	16
Betelgeuse	5 52·5	+7 24	0·9	−2·7, −2·2	1,200	650
α Crucis	12 23·8	−62 49	1·0	−2·9	1,000, 650	270
Aldebaran	4 33·0	+16 25	0·8	−0·1	90	65
Pollux	7 42·3	+28 09	1·2	+1·2	28	35
Spica	13 22·6	−10 54	1·0	−3·3	1,500	220
Antares	16 26·4	−26 19	1·0	−4·0	3,400	400
Fomalhaut	22 54·9	−29 53	1·2	2·0	13·5	23
Deneb	20 39·7	+45 06	1·3	−5·2	10,000	1,500
Regulus	10 05·7	+12 14	1·3	−0·2	70	85

Appendix IV

BOOKS ON TELESCOPES AND TELESCOPE-MAKING

Ingalls, A. G., ed. *Amateur Telescope Making Vol. I*. Scientific American, 1957.

King, H. C., *The History of the Telescope*. Griffin, 1955.

Kuiper, G. P., and Middlehurst, B. M. (edits.), *Telescopes*. Univ. Chicago Press, 1960.

Matthewson, G., *Constructing an Astronomical Telescope*. Pitman, 1955.

Miczaika, G. R., and Sinton, W. M., *Tools of the Astronomer*, Harvard Univ. Press, 1961.

Moore, P., and Murdin, P., *The Astronomer's Telescope*. Brockhampton, 1962.

Texereau, J., *How to Make a Telescope*. Interscience Publishers, 1957.

BOOKS FOR AMATEUR ASTRONOMERS

Moore, P. A., *The Amateur Astronomer*. Lutterworth, 1960.

Mayall, N., Mayall, M., and Wyckoff, J., *The Sky Observer's Guide*. Golden Press, N.Y., 1959.

Rackham, T., *Astronomical Photography at the Telescope*. Faber and Faber, 1959.

Sidgwick, J. B., *Amateur Astronomer's Handbook*. Faber and Faber, 1961.

Appendix V

SOCIETIES TO JOIN

Royal Astronomical Society. Aims at the encouragement and promotion of astronomy. Its main functions are to publish the results of astronomical and geophysical research, to maintain as complete a library as possible of astronomical literature, and to hold meetings in London and in other cities at which astronomical and geophysical matters can be discussed.

There are two ordinary classes of members: Fellows and Junior Members.

Address: Burlington House, Piccadilly, London, W.1.

British Astronomical Association. Has as its objects: (1) An association of observers, especially the possessors of small telescopes, for mutual help, and their organization in the work of astronomical observation. (2) The circulation of current astronomical information. (3) The encouragement of a popular interest in astronomy.

The Association holds its meetings at Burlington House, Piccadilly, where it has its own library. It publishes a *Journal*, *Handbook*, *Memoirs* and *Circulars*.

Registered Office: 303, Bath Road, Hounslow West, Middlesex.

Junior Astronomical Society. An organization formed to promote and encourage an interest in astronomy, and to provide instruction and assistance for beginners in the study of this science. The Society stands for all people, irrespective of age, who are beginners taking their first steps in astronomy. It publishes the journal *Hermes* not less than four times a year.

Hon. Secretary: E. W. Turner, 9, Hill View Road, Basingstoke, Hants.

British Interplanetary Society. Promotes the development of interplanetary exploration and communication by the study of rocket engineering, astronomy and other associated sciences. The Society organizes meetings, visits, lectures, exhibitions and film shows, and publishes a *Journal* and *Spaceflight*. Membership is open to anyone interested in astronautics, but Fellowship is restricted to those who possess some relevant scientific, technical or professional qualification.

Secretarial Address: 12, Bessborough Gardens, London, S.W.1.

Bibliography

Chapter 1

Baker, R. H., *Astronomy*. Van Nostrand, 1959.

Barlow, C. W. C., and Bryan, G. H., *Elementary Mathematical Astronomy*. University Tutorial Press, 1956.

Edwards, L., *The Spangled Heavens*. Bodley Head, 1955.

Evans, D. S., *Teach Yourself Astronomy*. English Univ. Press, 1952.

King, H. C., *Astronomy*. Vista Books, 1960.

Mehlin, T. G., *Astronomy*. John Wiley, N.Y., 1959.

Smart, W. M., *Spherical Astronomy*. Camb. Univ. Press, 1956.

Werner, H., *From the Aratus Globe to the Zeiss Planetarium*. V. G. Fischer, Stuttgart, 1957.

Chapter 2

Barlow, C. W. C., and Bryan, G. H., *Elementary Mathematical Astronomy*. University Tutorial Press, 1956.

Callatay, V. de, *Atlas of the Sky*. Macmillan, 1958.

Inglis, J. G. and R. M. G., *An Easy Guide to the Constellations*. Gall and Inglis, no date.

Peck, W., *The Constellations and How to Find Them*. Gall and Inglis, 1955.

Smart, W. M., *Spherical Astronomy*. Camb. Univ. Press, 1956.

Staal, J. D. W., *Patterns in the Sky*. Hodder and Stoughton, 1961.

Tancock, E. O., *Philips' Chart of the Stars*. Geo. Philip & Son, Ltd., 1958.

Webb, E. J., *The Names of the Stars*. Nisbet, 1952.

Widmann, W., and Schütte, K., *Guide to Stars*. Thames and Hudson, 1957.

Chapter 3

Abetti, G., *The Sun*. Faber and Faber, 1957.

Barlow, C. W. C., and Bryan, G. H., *Elementary Mathematical Astronomy*. University Tutorial Press, 1956.

Ellison, M. A., *The Sun and its Influence*. Routledge and Kegan Paul, 1959.

Menzel, D. H., *Our Sun*. Oxford Univ. Press, 1959.

Newton, H. W., *The Face of the Sun*. Pelican Books, 1959.

Smart, W. M., *Spherical Astronomy*. Camb. Univ. Press, 1956.

Chapter 4

Branley, F. M., *The Moon*. Thomas Crowell, N.Y. 1960.

Fielder, G., *Structure of the Moon's Surface*. Pergamon, 1961.

Firsoff, V. A., *Strange World of the Moon*. Hutchinson, 1959.

Firsoff, V. A., *Surface of the Moon*. Hutchinson, 1961.

King-Hele, D., *Satellites and Scientific Research*. Routledge and Kegan Paul, 1960.

Kopal, Z., *The Moon*. Chapman and Hall, 1960.

Moore, P., and Murdin, P., *The Astronomer's Telescope*. Brockhampton, 1962.

Wilkins, H. P., and Moore, P., *The Moon*. Faber and Faber, 1955.

Chapter 5

Branley, F. M., *The Nine Planets*. Thomas Crowell, N.Y., 1958.

King, H. C., *Worlds in Space*. Brockhampton, 1962.

Moore, P., *The Planet Venus*. Faber and Faber, 1961.

Peek, B. M., *The Planet Jupiter*. Faber and Faber, 1958.

Vaucouleurs, G. de., *The Planet Mars*. Faber and Faber, 1950.

Watson, F. G., *Between the Planets*. Oxford Univ. Press, 1956.

Whipple, F. L., *Earth, Moon, and Planets*. Oxford Univ. Press, 1958.

Chapter 6

Campbell, L., and Jacchia, L., *The Story of Variable Stars*. Oxford Univ. Press, 1941.

King, H. C., *Look at the Stars*. Hamish Hamilton, 1960.

Moore, P., *Stars and Space*. Black, 1960.

Payne-Gaposchkin, C., *Stars in the Making*. Eyre & Spottiswoode, 1953.

Payne-Gaposchkin, C., *Introduction to Astronomy*. Eyre & Spottiswoode, 1956.

Struve, O., *Elementary Astronomy*. Oxford Univ. Press, 1959.

Chapter 7

Bok, B. J., and Bok, P. F., *The Milky Way*. Oxford Univ. Press, 1957.

Davies, R. D., and Palmer, H. P., *Radio Studies of the Universe*, Routledge, 1959.

Hubble, E. P., *The Realm of the Nebulae*. Dover, 1958.

Lovell, A. C. B., *The Individual and the Universe*. Harper, N.Y., 1959.

Lyttleton, R. A., *The Modern Universe*. Hodder and Stoughton, 1956.

Shapley, H., *Galaxies*. Oxford Univ. Press, 1943.

Vaucouleurs, G. de., *Discovery of the Universe*. Faber & Faber, 1957.